Electronics
Handbook
For
The
Electrician

Leo G. Sands is the author or co-author of the following Chilton books of related interest: "Guide to Mobile Radio," "VHF-FM Marine Radio," "Portable FM Radiotelephones," and a forthcoming book on the selection, installation, and maintenance of air conditioners.

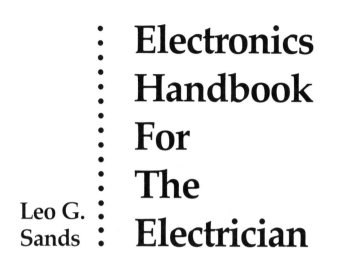

Electronics Handbook For The Electrician

Leo G. Sands

• CHILTON BOOK COMPANY

PHILADELPHIA   NEW YORK   LONDON

• Preface

Electronics is now of interest to a much larger segment of the public than ever before because almost everyone makes use of electronic devices. Before the term "electronics" was coined by the late Dr. Orestes Caldwell and used as the name of a magazine, electronics was a combination of radio and electrical technology.

Electronics is based on the "electron," a negatively-charged, minute particle. To understand electronics, it is not necessary to be a physicist. If the reader of this book will assume that the statements made here are true, without wondering why, an understanding of basic electronics will be easy. The basic point is that an electron is supposed to be a tiny particle that is attracted by, and that moves toward an object that is at a positive potential with respect to an electron.

The entire subject of electronics cannot be covered in one volume, nor even in a set of volumes. Electronics technology is constantly changing. What was considered true or up-to-date yesterday may not be so today. Only a short time ago, the transistor represented the latest state of the art. Now, the integrated circuit (IC) is making transistors and printed circuit boards obsolete. No one person can keep up with all the advancements in electronics. Therefore, in this book, the author attempts to explain basic electronics theory and practice in simple terms, but in sufficient depth to give the reader a basic understanding of the art.

This book was written specifically for the electrician who is now faced with the task of specifying, installing, and maintaining electronic equipment and systems.

The first chapter explains the differences between electrical and electronics terminology and circuitry. Chapters 2 and 3 cover the electronic applications of resistance, inductance, and capacitance, individually and in combination. Chapters 4, 5, 6, and 7 cover active electronic devices, which the British call "valves" and which Americans refer to as tubes and semiconductors.

Chapter 8 describes basic electronic systems, which consist of system components and subsystems. Chapter 9 describes basic electronics maintenance techniques, and Chapter 10 is a cyclopedia describing numerous electronic devices and circuits.

This book is intended to provide the electrician with a basic understanding of electronics, a platform on which he can build his knowledge of this constantly changing art.

Leo G. Sands

• Contents

• **Preface**   v

1 • **Electronic Diagrams and Terminology.**   1

Block Diagrams. Schematic Diagrams. Block-Schematics. Wiring Diagrams. Pictorial Diagrams. Electronics Terms.

2 • **Resistance in Electronic Circuits.**   13

Resistance. Variable Resistors. Fixed Resistors. Summary.

3 • **Inductance and Capacitance.**   32

Electromechanical Devices. Inductors. Capacitors. L-C. Circuits.

4 • **Diodes.**   55

Semiconductors. Thermionic Diodes.

5 • **Tubes.**   72

Triodes. Pentodes. Heptodes. Indicator Tubes. Triple Output Tubes. Gated Beam Tubes.

6 • Transistors.   103

      Analog Applications. Summary.

7 • Electronic Switch and Control Elements.   115

      DC Circuits. AC Circuits.

8 • Basic Electronic Systems.   121

      Control Systems. Monitoring Systems. Communications. Computers. System Components. Transmission Media. Summary.

9 • Electronic System Maintenance.   144

      Test Equipment. Personnel. Preventive Maintenance. Troubleshooting. Repairs. Summary.

10 • Electronic Devices and Circuits.   157

Electronics
Handbook
For
The
Electrician

1 : Electronic Diagrams And Terminology

Different circuit symbols are used by the electrical and electronics industries. And, to add to possible confusion, all of those engaged in the electronics field do not use the same symbols. Fortunately, electronics engineers and technicians are usually able to decipher schematic diagrams regardless of the symbols used.

• BLOCK DIAGRAMS

For the purpose of explanation of circuit functioning, block diagrams are often used. Generally, a single line (Fig. 1) is used to denote connections and signal paths between blocks representing circuit elements. Sometimes, arrowheads (Fig. 2) are used to denote the direction of signal flow.

Fig. 1. Typical block diagram.

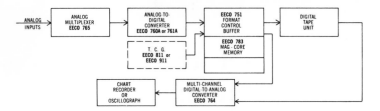

Fig. 2. Block diagram using arrowheads to denote direction of signal flow (Courtesy of Electronic Engineering Co. of California).

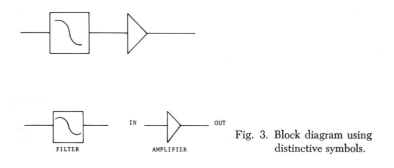

Fig. 3. Block diagram using distinctive symbols.

The blocks can all be rectangles, identified by appropriate labeling, or differently shaped blocks (Fig. 3) can be used to denote functions by shape.

• SCHEMATIC DIAGRAMS

A schematic diagram, of which Fig. 4 is an example, is supposed to indicate the actual circuitry used. However, terminal strips and tie-points are not shown, nor is it necessary that the interconnecting wires be shown as they actually run. A schematic is the most nearly definitive way to show an electronic circuit.

Symbols

The most commonly used electronic circuit symbols are

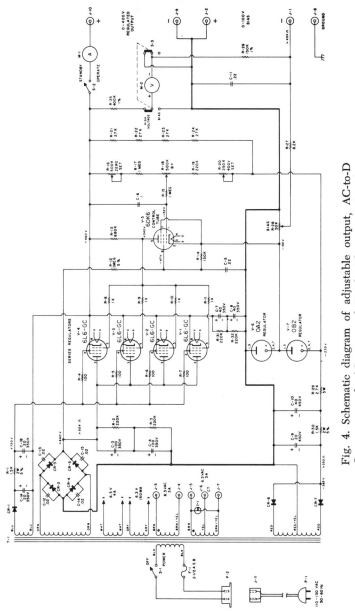

Fig. 4. Schematic diagram of adjustable output, AC-to-D C power supply (Courtesy of Knight Electronics Corp.).

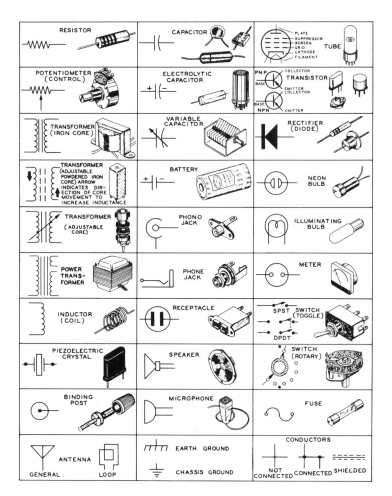

Fig. 5. Typical schematic symbols (Courtesy of Heath Co.).

given in Fig. 5. Depending on the draftsman, the engineer, and company policy, the symbol representing a transistor, for example, may appear with or without a circle around it. In most schematics, connection of one wire to another at a crossing point is indicated by a blob (Fig. 6). But when the drafts-

4

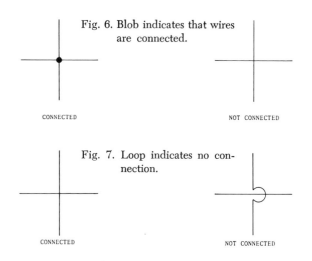

Fig. 6. Blob indicates that wires are connected.

CONNECTED

NOT CONNECTED

Fig. 7. Loop indicates no connection.

CONNECTED

NOT CONNECTED

man uses the other technique, the absence of a blob at a crossing point indicates that the two wires are connected, and to indicate that they are not connected, one line is shown looped over the other, as in Fig. 7.

• BLOCK-SCHEMATICS

For purposes of explanation of circuit functioning in greater depth, so-called block-schematic diagrams are used. Figure 8 is a typical example.

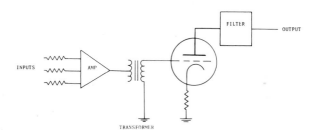

Fig. 8. Block schematic diagram.

5

• WIRING DIAGRAMS

For maintenance purposes, a wiring diagram (Fig. 9) can be extremely useful. For circuit operation explanation

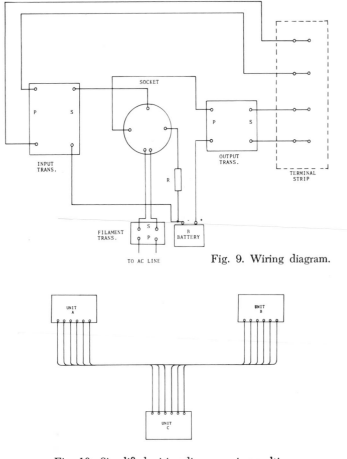

Fig. 9. Wiring diagram.

Fig. 10. Simplified wiring diagram using multi-conductor cable (leads identified by color code or number reg.).

purposes, such a diagram is very often useless. Some wiring diagrams use drafting short-cuts, as indicated in Fig. 10. Here, the individual conductors of a multiconductor cable or wiring harness are labeled, and it is expected that the viewer will understand that lead BW leading into the common line is the same conductor as lead BW broken out at some other point.

• PICTORIAL DIAGRAMS

Pictorial diagrams (Fig. 11) are furnished mostly with electronic kits and are intended to aid the assembler of the device.

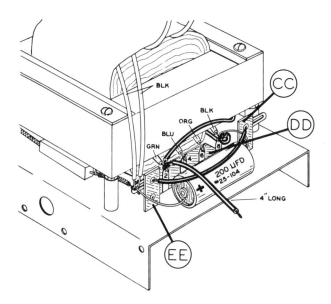

Fig. 11. Pictorial diagram (Courtesy of Heath Co.).

• ELECTRONICS TERMS

The electrician uses a language somewhat different from that used by electronics technicians and engineers. This is because there are more electronics terms and because electronics is concerned more with signals than with power. Table 1 lists some of the most commonly used electronics terms, and Chapter 10 contains more detailed descriptions of electronics terms.

Table 1(A)

BASIC ELECTRONIC TERMS

Phenomenon	Terms Used	Values
Amplification	Gain	Decibel (ratio of voltage, current or power amplification)
	Amplification Factor	Voltage or current multiplication
Power	Watts	Microwatts, milliwatts, watts or kilowatts
	Decibels	Decibels related to one milliwatt, one watt or one kilowatt
Potential (electrical)	Volts	Microvolts, millivolts, volts or kilovolts
	Decibels	Decibels related to a reference voltage level
Current	Amperes	Microamperes, milliamperes or amperes
Time	Seconds	Nanoseconds, microseconds or seconds

8

Frequency	Hertz	Hertz, kilohertz, megahertz or giga-hertz
Capacity	Farad	Picofarad or microfarad
Inductance	Henry	Microhenry, millihenry or henry
Impedance	Ohm	Ohm, kilo-ohm or megohm
Modulation	Frequency Modulation (FM)	Frequency deviation
	Amplitude Modulation (AM)	Modulation percentage

Table 1(B)

MULTIPLES AND SUBMULTIPLES OF ELECTRICAL VALUES

nano	trillionth	kilo	thousands
pico	billionth	mega	millions
micro	millionth	giga	billions
milli	thousandth		

Power

The electrician is accustomed to using such terms as kilo-watts, volt-amperes, and power factor. In electronics, the terms milliwatts, microwatts, dbm, and dbw are much more commonly used because most references are to "signal" power instead of operating power.

Voltage

The electrician is usually concerned with RMS (AC) and DC voltages, whereas, in electronics, peak and peak-to-peak voltages, as well as wave form, are often important considerations. Voltage levels in electronics are often in the millivolt and microvolt ranges.

9

Current

Amperes is an important term for electricians. But in electronics, milliampere, microampere, and even nanoampere are meaningful terms. Such small currents are often difficult to switch. Therefore, the term "dry circuit" is applicable to very low level signal circuits.

Phase

The electrician is concerned with phase mainly in connection with three-phase power circuits and power factor. But in electronics, phase shift and phase relationships may be of considerable importance.

Frequency

Most electricians are concerned only with 60 Hz (cycles per second) AC, some with 50 Hz AC, and a few with 25 Hz AC. But in electronics, frequency considerations range from DC to Gigahertz (billions of cycles per second). Also, those concerned with digital data must consider the term "baud," which represents bits per second.

Digital/Analog

Electrical power circuits, in general, are analog (stepless) in nature. So are most electronic circuits. However, there is growing utilization of digital devices. In broad terms, an analog device is considered as one in which current, voltage, and/or phase may vary in random or stepless fashion. In the case of a digital device, current, voltage, and/or phase changes in discrete steps or is absent, present, or abruptly reversed. For example, a radio is an analog device, whereas a telephone dial is one type of digital device.

Passive

A passive device is one that has no moving parts or does not generate power or a signal. L-C (inductive-capacitive) and R-C (resistive-capacitive) networks or filters are considered passive.

10

Active

A tube, a transistor, and an electromechanical device (such as a relay) are all considered active elements. For example, an L-C filter is considered passive, whereas an electronic filter (employing tubes or transistors) is considered active.

Electron Flow

The electrician usually has been taught to believe that electric current flow is from positive to negative. But in the electronics field, it is considered that electrons flow from negative to positive. So, let us assume, for the sake of compatible thinking, that both electrons and electric current flow in the same direction—from negative to positive. Otherwise, understanding electronics can be confusing.

Other Terms

Chapter 10 of this book contains a description of terms, devices, and circuits with which an electrician may not be familiar, and Table 2 lists basic electronic devices.

Table 2

BASIC ELECTRONIC DEVICES

Device	Function	Applications
Amplifier, AF	Amplifies AC signals from 50 Hz to 15 Khz (approx.)	Sound reinforcement and control signal amplification.
Amplifier, DC	Amplifies both DC and AC.	Control and instrumentation.
Amplifier, RF	Amplifies RF signals at a specific frequency or over a band of frequencies.	In radio equipment.

Logic Circuit	Makes logical decisions (AND, OR, NOR, NOT, NAND, etc.)	Digital control systems and computers.
Receiver	Intercepts and amplifies signals at a specific frequency or over a band of frequencies.	Radio, control, and data systems.
Transmitter	Generates a modulated or unmodulated signal at a specific frequency.	Radio, control, and data systems.
Transducer	Converts physical changes into an electrical signal or vice versa.	For sensing physical changes or converting electrical signals into sound or physical motion.

2 : Resistance In Electronic Circuits

Electricians are usually more concerned with electromagnetic devices than with purely resistive devices, with the exception of incandescent lamps. Such lamps are resistive devices the resistance of which varies with filament temperature. In electronics, lamps are used in some circuits where their variable resistance characteristics are required, but they are used mainly as status indicators.

Both fixed and variable resistors are used in electronic devices. Their resistance varies to a limited degree with temperature, but this characteristic is generally not desired. There are also resistive devices used in electronics the resistance of which varies widely with temperature (thermistor), light (photoelectric cell), and voltage (varistor). Where these devices are used, the variable resistance characteristics are desired.

• **RESISTANCE**

Electric current flows when there is a voltage (difference in electrical potential) and a conducting path. Copper, silver, aluminum, and many other metals are good electrical conductors. Copper and aluminum are most commonly used. An insulator is a material, such as air, glass, mica, or wood, which is a very poor conductor.

The amount of current flowing in a circuit depends on the voltage and the resistance of the circuit. According to Ohm's law, 1 ampere will flow through a resistance of 1 ohm when 1 volt is applied $(I = E/R)$.* Hence, if a lamp is connected across a 1.5-volt flashlight cell, 0.5 ampere will flow through the lamp and the battery if the resistance of the lamp is 3 ohms $(1.5/3 = 0.5)$.

The battery itself and the wires leading to the lamp also have resistance. This resistance is so small that it can often be ignored. But if a lamp with a very low resistance is connected across the cell, say 0.15 ohm, it could be assumed that the current would be 10 amperes $(1.5/0.15 = 10)$. But if the internal resistance of the cell is 0.1 ohm, the current will be only 6 amperes. The resistance of the lamp (R1) and the internal resistance of the cell (R2) are in series and are added to each other, as shown in Fig. 12.

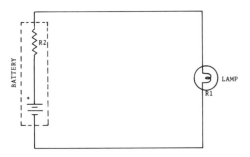

Fig. 12. Internal resistance of battery is in series with load.

* I is current in amperes; E is potential in volts; R is resistance in ohms.

Every material has some resistance. Silver has less resistance than copper. Iron has considerably more resistance than copper. Resistors are used in electrical and electronic circuits to reduce current and voltage. Resistors are made of carbon, iron wire, and other materials that are poorer conductors than copper.

Resistors in Series

When resistors are connected in series, as shown in Fig. 13, their total resistance is equal to the sum of their individual resistances. For example, if R1 is 2 ohms, R2 is 4 ohms, and R3 is 6 ohms, then their total resistance is 12 ohms (2 + 4 + 6 = 12). If E (battery voltage) is 12 volts, the current through all of the resistors is equal and is 1 ampere when the internal resistance of the battery is ignored.

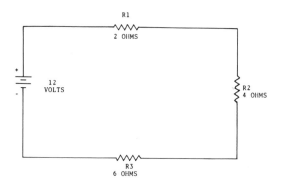

Fig. 13. Current through all elements of a series circuit is the same.

The voltage across each resistor will be different. There will be 2 volts across R1, 4 volts across R2, and 6 volts across R3. The sum of the voltage-drops in a series circuit is equal to the source voltage (12 volts in this case).

The voltage-drop across each resistor is equal to the current multiplied by the resistance ($E = IR$). If the resistance is 5

15

ohms and the current is 2 amperes, the voltage across the resistance will be 10 volts.

Resistors in Parallel

When resistors are connected in parallel, their total resistance is reduced. When two 5-ohm resistances are connected in parallel, their combined resistance will be 2.5 ohms. To calculate the resistance of two unlike resistances in parallel, use the formula:

$$R = \frac{R1 \times R2}{R1 + R2}$$

If R1 is 2 ohms and R2 is 6 ohms, R will be 1.5 ohms, since $2 \times 6 = 12$ and $2 + 6 = 8$, and 12 divided by 8 equals 1.5.

In the circuit shown in Fig. 14, the current through the lamp (with a resistance of 50 ohms) is approximately 0.2 ampere. The total circuit resistance is 40 ohms, since 7 ohms (R1) plus 33 ohms (R2 and the lamp in parallel) equals 40. The circuit current is 0.3 ampere, since 12 divided by 40 equals 0.3. The voltage-drop across R1 is 2.1 volts, since 7 ohms times 0.3 ampere equals 2.1. Therefore, the source voltage (12 volts) minus the 2.1-volt drop in R1 leaves 9.9 volts

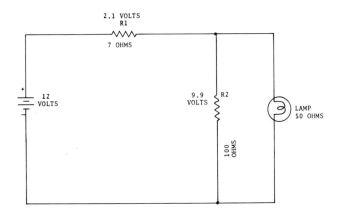

Fig. 14. Series–parallel circuit.

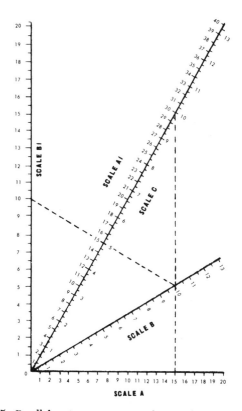

Fig. 15. Parallel resistance nomograph. Use this nomograph to determine the resistance of two or three resistors in parallel. For two resistors, lay a straight edge at the known resistance on scale A and the other known resistance on scale A1. Their combined resistance will be indicated by the point of contact of the straight edge on scale B. For a third resistor, place a straight edge at scale B at the point where the answer for two resistors was obtained, and on scale B1 for the known value of the third resistor. The answer will be on scale C. (Courtesy of Memcor, Inc.)

across R2 and the lamp (in parallel). Thus, the current through the lamp is 0.2 ampere, since 9.9 volts divided by 50 ohms equals 0.199 ampere.

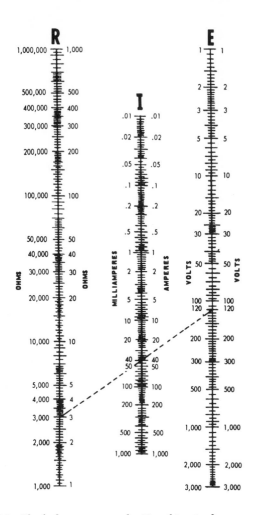

Fig. 16. Ohm's law nomograph. Use this simple nomograph for solving Ohm's law problems. To determine resistance, place a straight edge at the two known quantities (volts and amperes) and read the answer on the ohm scale. To determine current, use the same techniques and read current on the amperes or milliamperes scale. (Courtesy of Memcor, Inc.)

A lamp is shown here as an example, and its resistance is considered as being of a fixed value. Actually, the resistance of the lamp varies, rising as the voltage across it increases. To determine quickly the resistance of two or three resistors in parallel, use the nomogram, Fig. 15.

Power Consumption

The total power consumed from the battery is 3.6 watts ($P = EI$). When E (voltage) is 12 volts and I (current) is 0.3 ampere, P equals 3.6 watts. Of this total, 0.63 watt is absorbed by R1 (2.1 volts times 0.3 ampere). The power absorbed by R2 is 0.98 watt, since P is also equal to $E2/R$, and, in this case, $E = 9.9$ volts and $R = 100$, and $9.9 \times 9.9 = 98.01$, which, divided by 100, equals 0.98.

We can see that 0.63 watt consumed by R1 and 0.98 watt consumed by R2 totals 1.61 watts. Thus, the lamp must consume about 2 watts if the total power consumption is 3.6 watts. Power is also equal to I^2R. If the current through the lamp is 0.2 ampere and its resistance is 50 ohms, its power consumption is 2 watts. Figure 16 is a nomogram for determining resistance and current.

Resistor Ratings

Resistors are rated in ohms and in power handling capacity as well as resistance accuracy (tolerance). Since R1 in Fig. 14 must dissipate 0.63 watt, a 1-watt resistor should be used. The power R2 must dissipate is 0.98 watt, which is almost 1 watt. It is safer to use a 2-watt resistor.

Carbon composition resistors are coded by color bands that indicate resistance and tolerance. The color code is given in Fig. 17. A 100,000-ohm resistor would be coded brown-black-yellow. If there is no fourth color band, it has a tolerance of 20%, meaning that its resistance could be anywhere from 80,000 to 120,000 ohms. A silver band (fourth color band) indicates 10% tolerance (90,000 to 110,000 ohms), and a gold fourth band indicates 5% tolerance (95,000 to 105,000 ohms).

For many purposes, a 20% tolerance resistor is adequate.

EIA/MIL COLOR CODE

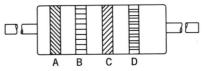

Band A—1st significant figure
Band B—2nd significant figure
Band C—Number of zeros or decimal multiplier
Band D—Tolerance

Color	Significant Figure	Multiplying Value
Black	0	1
Brown	1	10
Red	2	100
Orange	3	1,000
Yellow	4	10,000
Green	5	100,000
Blue	6	1,000,000
Violet	7	10,000,000
Gray	8	100,000,000
White	9	1,000,000,000
Gold	±5% tolerance	0.1
Silver	±10% tolerance	0.01
No color	±20% tolerance	

Fig. 17.
Fig. 18. Carbon resistor.

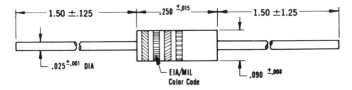

But many circuits require 5% or 10% resistors, and in some applications (such as meters), special 1% tolerance resistors must be used.

Carbon composition resistors (Fig. 18) are used in most electronic circuits where they are required to handle less than 2 watts. Wire-wound resistors (Fig. 19) are used in higher power circuits and are available in ratings up to 1,500 watts or more.

20

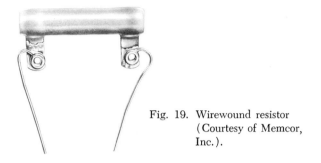

Fig. 19. Wirewound resistor (Courtesy of Memcor, Inc.).

• VARIABLE RESISTORS

Rheostats

A rheostat is a variable resistor. A rheostat can be used in a circuit, such as the one shown in Fig. 20, to make it possible to adjust the brilliance of a lamp. If the rheostat has a 0 to 100 ohm range, the lamp current can be reduced to half when all of the rheostat resistance is in the circuit. The voltage-drop across R (the rheostat) is varied as it is adjusted. The sum of the voltage-drop E1 across R and the voltage E2 across the lamp always equals the source voltage. Thus, as the resistance of R is increased, E1 rises and E2 falls.

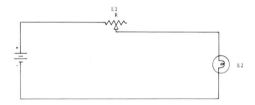

Fig. 20. Rheostat used for controlling load voltage and current.

Potentiometers

A potentiometer is similar to a rheostat except that it has three terminals, as shown in Fig. 5. A potentiometer can function as a rheostat with the use of only two of its terminals or with strapping of the contact arm to one end of the resistance element.

In Fig. 21, the lamp is shunted by a part of the potentiometer resistance element. The other part of the resistance element is in series with the circuit. If the potentiometer has a value of 200 ohms, there will be 100 ohms (R1) in series with the circuit, and 100 ohms shunted across the lamp when the potentiometer is set to the mid-resistance point and switch S is closed.

The total circuit resistance will be 133 ohms, 100 ohms in series with 33 ohms. The 33-ohm resistance exists when the 50-ohm lamp is shunted by 100 ohms of the potentiometer resistance. The total circuit current is 0.09 ampere (12 volts divided by 133 ohms). The voltage-drop across R1, the part of the potentiometer resistance in series with the circuit, is 9 volts (100 ohms times 0.09 ampere).

Basic Equations

$$I = \frac{E}{R} \quad R = \frac{E}{I} \quad E = RI \quad P = I^2R \quad P = \frac{E^2}{R}$$

I = Current in amperes   R = Resistance in ohms
E = Potential in volts   P = Power in watts

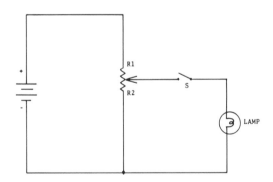

Fig. 21. Potentiometer used as variable voltage divider.

Therefore, the potential across the lamp is 3 volts (12 volts minus 9 volts). The lamp thus consumes 0.18 watt (3 volts times 3 volts divided by 50 ohms). Section R1 of the potentiometer consumes 0.81 watt (9 volts times 9 volts divided by 100 ohms). Section R2 of the potentiometer consumers 0.09 watt (3 volts times 3 volts divided by 100 ohms). The potentiometer must handle 0.9 watt when set at its mid–resistance point.

However, when the potentiometer is adjusted so that the R1 section resistance is reduced to 10 ohms and the R2 section is increased to 190 ohms, the circuit current (through R1) rises to 0.24 ampere. The power dissipated in the R1 section of the potentiometer drops to 0.576 watt, but if a potentiometer rated at 2 watts is used, it will be overloaded. The power–handling capacity of the potentiometer is based on maximum current, considering the entire resistance. Thus, the 0.24–ampere current through any portion of the potentiometer would require it to be capable of handling almost 3 watts (0.24 × 12 = 2.88).

When switch S is opened to remove the lamp from the circuit, the voltage across the R2 portion of the potentiometer is directly proportional to its resistance ratio. If it is set so that R1 is 10 ohms and R2 is 190 ohms, the voltage across R2 will be 11.4 volts, and across R1 it will be 0.6 volt. But when switch S is again closed, the voltage across the R2 portion of the potentiometer (and the lamp) will drop to 9.6 volts, since the voltage–drop across the R1 portion of the potentiometer rises to 2.4 volts because of the increased current through it (0.24 ampere).

Voltage Dividers

Resistors R1 and R2 in Fig. 14 form a fixed voltage divider. The potentiometer in Fig. 21 is a variable voltage divider. A more complex voltage divider circuit is shown in Fig. 22. The values of the resistors can be calculated so that the required voltages will be provided. But if the current drawn from any of the voltage taps is raised or lowered, the voltages will be

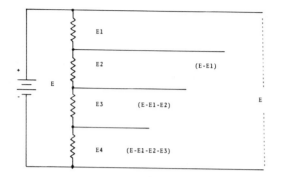

Fig. 22. Fixed multi-outputs voltage divider.

affected, since the voltage-drop across the resistors will change because of a change in current through them.

So far, we have used the terms volts, amperes, ohms, and watts. In electronics, variations of these terms, such as milli-amperes and milliwatts, are used.

Level Controls

A potentiometer is often used for adjusting the output level of an electronic amplifier by variation of its gain (amount of amplification), input and output signal levels, or circuit op-erating voltages.

A radio volume control is used to adjust the sound level at a loudspeaker or set of headphones. It is usually connected at the output of the detector, as shown in block diagram (Fig. 23). It is a potentiometer functioning as a voltage divider. The level of audio voltage fed to the audio amplifier depends on the strength of the incoming radio signal, its percentage of modulation, and the setting of the volume control.

A potentiometer with a so-called audio taper is used to provide logarithmic adjustment. If a linear taper were used,

Fig. 23. Radio volume control is usually a voltage divider at output of detector.

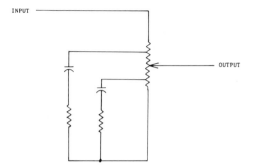

Fig. 24. Frequency-compensated volume control.

the voltage adjustment would be linear; but the ear does not perceive sound in a linear way, and only a small portion of the potentiometer rotation would be effective.

In some radio receivers, the volume control resistance element has one or more taps, as shown in Fig. 24. It thus provides frequency response correction at various volume levels to compensate for the characteristics of the human ear.

Volume level can also be controlled at the receiver output. This is done in trunk-mounted mobile radio units and in train radio installations. This arrangement eliminates the need for running audio input wires, which are sensitive to noise and hum pickup, to the remote volume control. A potentiometer can be used, as shown in Fig. 25. The impedance of the load, however, varies. When set to the maximum volume position, the potentiometer and loudspeaker are paralleled directly across the output transformer secondary. When set for low

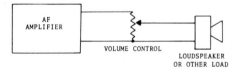

Fig. 25. Level control at output of amplifier.

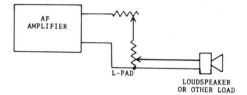

Fig. 26. "L" pad maintains a constant load on the source.

volume level, the potentiometer divides the signal voltage, and the total load impedance is increased.

"L" Pads

With the use of an "L" pad, as shown in Fig. 26, the voltage level fed to the speaker or other load can be varied, but the total load impedance ("L" and speaker), looking back at the source, remains constant, since the "L" pad adds series resistance in one section as it shunts the load with the other section. An "L" pad usually consists of two potentiometers ganged and rotated by a common shaft.

"T" Pads

A "T" pad, on the other hand, usually employs three ganged potentiometers (or rheostats), and maintains constant impedance looking back into the source (output transformer) and into the load (loudspeaker). It is connected as shown in Fig. 27.

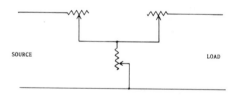

Fig. 27. "T" pad maintains constant impedance looking into the source as well as the load.

Faders

A fader is a tapped potentiometer that can be used to select either of two signals, as shown in Fig. 28. With the use of an untapped potentiometer in an auto radio application, for example, either of two speakers can be selected, or both can be operated simultaneously, as shown in Fig. 29.

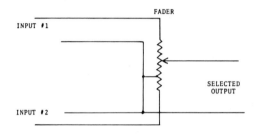

Fig. 28. Fader allows selection and adjustment of level of either of two signals.

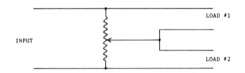

Fig. 29. Potentiometer can be used to select, vary the level, or mix a single signal into two loads.

Amplification Control

The gain of an amplifier can be controlled by variation of the level of one or more operating (not signal) voltages with a potentiometer connected as shown in Fig. 30. Potentiometer R1 varies the cathode bias on the amplifier tube, which controls gain. A screen grid voltage control (R2) can be used to control gain. The gain is decreased by lowering the screen voltage. This technique is used mainly with sharp cut-off tetrode or pentode tubes, whereas the cathode circuit control

27

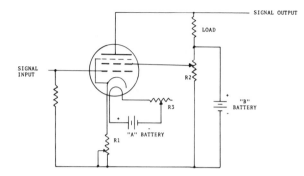

Fig. 30. Amplification can be controlled by adjustment of operating voltages.

is used with remote cut-off tubes. A sharp cut-off tube is one which can be biased to cut off (plate current falls to zero), whereas the plate current of a remote cut-off tube drops off gradually as bias is increased and is not cut off until the bias is quite high.

Gain can also be controlled by variation of tube filament (heater) current with a rheostat (R3), as shown in Fig. 30. In early radios, the volume control varied the filament current of two or three RF amplifier stages.

The gain control has many names, depending on how it is used and on its type. Most often, it is an input level control. Sometimes, it is an amplification control, and it can be an attenuator, such as an "L" pad or "T" pad.

• FIXED RESISTORS

All of the controls described above are variable resistors (potentiometers or rheostats). Electronic devices employ fixed resistors as well as manually variable resistors and resistive transducers (such as thermistors).

Carbon Resistors

The most commonly used resistor is the carbon composition

28

type. It has connecting leads at each end, as previously shown in Fig. 18. These resistors are color coded (Fig. 17). The rated resistance can be determined by the color code. The accuracy of the resistance rating can be noted by the color of the tolerance band.

A 100-ohm resistor with a 5% tolerance rating may actually have a resistance as low as 95 ohms or as high as 105 ohms. A 100-ohm, 20% resistor may have a resistance within the 80 to 120 ohm range. Table 3 lists the standard values of carbon resistors.

Table 3

STANDARD RESISTOR VALUES

			Ohms				Meghoms	
	1.0	10	100	1,000	10,000	0.1	1.0	10.0
	1.1	11	110	1,100	11,000	0.11	1.1	11.0
	1.2	12	120	1,200	12,000	0.12	1.2	12.0
	1.3	13	130	1,300	13,000	0.13	1.3	13.0
	1.5	15	150	1,500	15,000	0.15	1.5	15.0
	1.6	16	160	1,600	16,000	0.16	1.6	16.0
	1.8	18	180	1,800	18,000	0.18	1.8	18.0
	2.0	20	200	2,000	20,000	0.20	2.0	20.0
	2.2	22	220	2,200	22,000	0.22	2.2	22.0
0.24	2.4	24	240	2,400	24,000	0.24	2.4	
0.27	2.7	27	270	2,700	27,000	0.27	2.7	
0.30	3.0	30	300	3,000	30,000	0.30	3.0	
0.33	3.3	33	330	3,300	33,000	0.33	3.3	
0.36	3.6	36	360	3,600	36,000	0.36	3.6	
0.39	3.9	39	390	3,900	39,000	0.39	3.9	
0.43	4.3	43	430	4,300	43,000	0.43	4.3	
0.47	4.7	47	470	4,700	47,000	0.47	4.7	
0.51	5.1	51	510	5,100	51,000	0.51	5.1	
0.56	5.6	56	560	5,600	56,000	0.56	5.6	
0.62	6.2	62	620	6,200	62,000	0.62	6.2	
0.68	6.8	68	680	6,800	68,000	0.68	6.8	
0.75	7.5	75	750	7,500	75,000	0.75	7.5	
0.82	8.2	82	820	8,200	82,000	0.82	8.2	
0.91	9.1	91	910	9,100	91,000	0.91	9.1	

Carbon composition resistors are available in power handling ratings from 1/10 to 2 watts. Their resistance is affected by heat, and they are considered noninductive (no inductive reactance). At extremely high frequencies, the leads alone add significant inductance.

Wire-wound Resistors

Wire-wound resistors are generally used when power handling requirements are greater than the capacity of the carbon types. A wire-wound resistor consists of highly resistive wire (such as nichrome) wound on an insulated bobbin. The wire is often impregnated with a vitreous material for insulating purposes.

These resistors are available with wire leads or solder terminals. Some are provided with a sliding tap that permits variation of the resistance or the formation of a fixed potentiometer (voltage divider).

There are also deposited carbon and metallic film resistors, used in fairly sophisticated equipment.

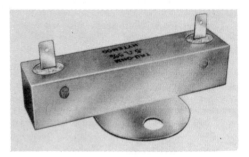

Fig. 31. Ballast resistor.

Ballast Resistors

Incandescent lamps are sometimes used as resistors. However, their resistance increases with filament temperature. Ballast tubes and resistors, such as the one shown in Fig. 31, take advantage of this effect to regulate current.

Thermistors

A thermistor is a temperature-sensitive resistor. The resistance of a carbon resistor rises slightly with temperature, whether environmental or the result of self-heating.

Varistors

A varistor is a voltage-sensitive resistor: resistance falls as the voltage across it rises.

• SUMMARY

Resistors are used in electronic devices to reduce voltage (signal or operating potential) and to limit current, as well as for signal isolation and mixing purposes. Fixed resistors are used by the billions each year. Variable resistors are used for controlling signal and operating voltage levels and for altering the operating characteristics of electronic devices, as well as for mixing signals.

3 : Inductance
And
Capacitance

Next to resistors, inductors and capacitors are the most widely used passive electronic components. They are used mainly in circuits in which AC is involved. In DC circuits, capacitors function as storage devices, and inductors are primarily used in electromechanical devices.

- **ELECTROMECHANICAL DEVICES**

If a coil of wire is wound and connected to a battery, a strong magnetic field is produced. The strength of the magnetic field becomes greater as the number of ampere-turns is increased. To strengthen the field, increase the current or the number of turns in the coil, or both.

A solenoid is simply a coil inside of which is an iron or steel plunger that is moved by the magnetic field toward the area of greatest magnetism.

If a coil of wire is wound around an iron core, an electromagnet is formed. As shown in Fig. 32, a coil may be wound around a nail. When switch S is closed, a fairly powerful magnet is formed.

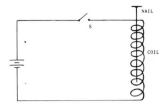

Fig. 32. Simple electromagnet.

Relays

The most common application of electromagnetism in DC circuits is the relay, as shown in Fig. 33. A simple relay employs an iron core (pole piece) with a coil of wire around it. When current flows through the coil, the iron core is magnetized, causing the relay armature to be pulled in toward it. When the current flow is cut off, the armature is pulled back away from the pole piece by a spring. By mechanical coupling of a switch assembly to the armature, a relay (electromagnetic switch) is formed.

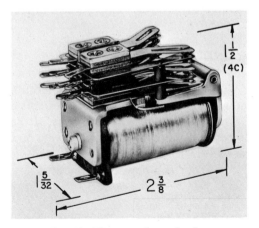

Fig. 33. Electromechanical relay.

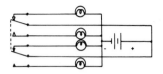

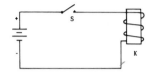

Fig. 34. A relay can control several circuits. Here,
one SPST switch controls four lamps.

Relays are used in electronic devices to control circuits that are electrically isolated from the controlling switch. In Fig. 34, for example, a single SPST switch (S) controls a relay (K), which in turn controls several circuits.

Direct current (DC) flows through a coil of wire and is limited by the resistance of the wire. A magnetic field is developed around the coil when current is applied. The field collapses when the current is cut off. As the field collapses, an inductive kick is produced, which, as will be seen later, allows the employment of electromagnetism in many ways.

• INDUCTORS

Coils used in radio and other electronic circuits are also known as inductances, inductors, reactors and, if they have two or more windings, as transformers. If they are used in audio or power circuits, they usually have a laminated iron core. Those used in RF (radio frequency) and video circuits may have an air core or a powdered iron core.

DC Circuits

As stated earlier, a magnetic field is developed around a coil when direct current (DC) flows through it. When a DC

34

voltage is applied to a coil, the current through the coil at first is zero. The current rises gradually to a value limited by the resistance of the circuit. The time required for the current to reach its maximum value is known as the time constant of the coil, which is equal to L/R.

A coil of any type has some resistance, even if it is made of heavy silver wire, since no material is a perfect electrical conductor. A coil with many turns of fine wire will have more resistance than one with fewer turns of heavier wire. The resistance of a coil is a liability, not an asset. The higher the resistance of a coil, the lower is its efficiency.

Current rises slowly because a counter-electromotive force (voltage) is induced in a coil whenever the current tends to change. The value of this counter-electromotive force depends on the inductance of the coil. Its polarity is opposite that of the applied DC voltage.

Inductance Value

It is the inductance of the coil that is important. The greater the number of turns in a coil, the higher the value of inductance (expressed in henries, millihenries, and microhenries). Inductance is also affected by the diameter of a coil, the spacing of its turns, and the kind of core. The inductance of an iron core coil is much greater than that of a coil with an air core. The higher the inductance, the longer it takes for current flowing through a coil to reach maximum value. Hence, the time constant of a coil increases as its inductance increases.

AC Circuits

Alternating current (AC) reverses its direction of current flow at a rate determined by its frequency. The polarity of the AC voltage also reverses. The level of the voltage rises and falls sinusoidally. At the beginning of a cycle, the voltage rises gradually to its peak value, then falls gradually to zero. It then rises in the opposite direction (reversed polarity) to its peak value and again goes back to zero. This cycle is repeated over and over again. In the case of domestic house cur-

35

rent, the voltage reverses polarity 60 times a second. The voltage of a radio signal may reverse polarity millions of times per second.

The commonly used voltage reference is RMS (root mean square) voltage. The peak voltage is 1.4 times greater. In the case of house current, for example, the RMS voltage is said to be approximately 115 volts. The peak voltage is 1.4 times 115, or 161 volts, and the peak-to-peak voltage is 322 volts.

When AC is applied to a perfect capacitor, the current leads voltage by 90° (one quarter of a cycle); or it can be said that voltage lags current by 90°. When AC is applied to a perfect inductance, the current lags the voltage by 90°; but when AC is applied to a resistor, the current and voltage are in phase with each other.

When AC is applied to a coil, the current is zero at the time the applied voltage is highest, and increases as the voltage drops. As the current rises, the magnetic field around the coil becomes stronger. The current reaches its maximum value when the voltage reaches zero. The current cannot continue to rise because the applied voltage now starts to rise in the other direction. It must tend to decrease, but at the same time, a voltage is induced which tries to keep the current flowing in its original direction. The current falls off slowly at first, and the magnetic field starts to get weaker. The current drops off more rapidly as the magnetic field weakens.

The current drops off to zero when the applied voltage reaches maximum in the reverse direction. At the same time, the induced voltage (counter-electromotive force) is at maximum value, but its polarity is opposite that of the applied voltage.

As the applied voltage starts to drop off, the current starts to flow in the opposite direction, and the magnetic field is again built up. Then, after the current has reached maximum, it again falls off, and the magnetic field weakens. The action is repeated over and over again.

The above process takes place when the coil is a pure inductance (has no resistance). Actually, there is no such thing.

Under ideal conditions, the induced voltage (counter-electromotive force) and the applied voltage are of opposite polarity, exactly 180° out of phase with each other. Under practical conditions, the phase relationships are not quite the same.

Because of the induced voltage, the current never reaches as high a value as when DC is applied to a coil. The inductance tends to oppose the flow of current when AC is applied. If the power transformer of an AC-operated electronic device is connected to a 115-volt DC line, the transformer will burn out, because the only opposition to current flow is the resistance of the transformer primary winding.

But if the device is connected to a 115-volt AC line, only a small current will flow because of the inductive reactance of the coil (transformer primary winding). The reactance of a coil depends on its inductance and the frequency of the AC voltage, and is equal to $2\pi FL$, where F is the frequency in Hz (cycles per second) and L is the inductance in henries.

Coils in Series

Two separate coils may be connected in series to provide increased inductance. The inductance of two coils wound on the same form (air core) or core is increased when the coils are wound in the same direction and connected in series, as

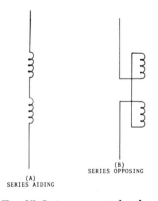

(A)
SERIES AIDING

(B)
SERIES OPPOSING

Fig. 35. Series–connected coils.

shown in Fig. 35(A). If they are wound in opposite directions or connected in series-opposite directions, or connected in series-opposing, as in Fig. 35(B), their combined inductance will be reduced.

Transformers

A transformer may have an air core (Fig. 36) or powdered iron core (Fig. 37) when used in RF or video circuits, or a laminated iron core when used in AF (audio frequency) or power circuits. It may have two or more windings. Power is fed into one winding, known as the primary, and taken out of another winding, known as the secondary, as shown in Fig. 38.

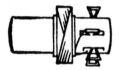

Fig. 36. Air core coil (Courtesy of Q-max Corp.).

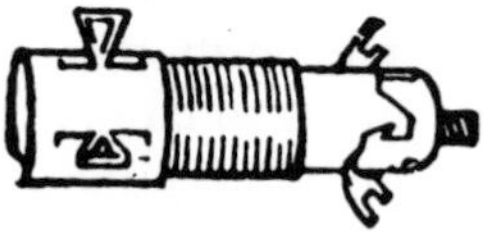

Fig. 37. Coil with adjustable ferrite core (Courtesy of Q-max Corp.).

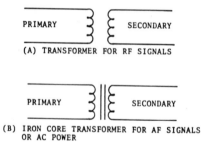

(A) TRANSFORMER FOR RF SIGNALS

(B) IRON CORE TRANSFORMER FOR AF SIGNALS OR AC POWER

Fig. 38. Two winding transformer.

The output voltage depends on the ratio of primary to secondary turns. If the primary has ten times as many turns as the secondary, the transformer has a 10:1 turns ratio and is known as a stepdown transformer. Thus, if the input voltage is 115 volts, the output voltage will be 11.5, provided the output current rating is not exceeded.

The primary envelops the secondary, inducing a voltage into it. There can be more than one secondary winding. If the primary of the transformer shown schematically in Fig. 38 (B) has 500 turns and the secondary has 25 turns, the voltage across L2 will be 6 volts if the input voltage is 120 volts, since the turns ratio is 500:25 or 20:1. If secondary L3 has 2,000 turns, the voltage across it will be 480 volts, since the L1 to L3 turns ratio is 500:20,000 or 1:4. L1 and L3 form a stepup transformer. Note that L3 has a center tap, which means that the voltage between the center tap and either end of L3 is 240 volts.

Autotransformers

An autotransformer has one winding which is tapped, as shown in Fig. 39. If section L1 has 100 turns, and 120 volts

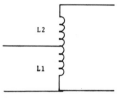

(A) AIR CORE AUTOTRANSFORMER

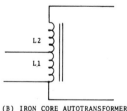

(B) IRON CORE AUTOTRANSFORMER

Fig. 39. Autotransformer.

39

is applied to L1, the output voltage across L1 and L2 will be 140 volts, since the turns ratio of L1 to L1 and L2 is 600:700, 120:140 or 6:7. This is a stepup autotransformer. By feeding the 120 volts to windings L1 and L2 and taking the output from L1, a stepdown autotransformer is formed. The turns ratio is 700:600 or 7:6, making the output voltage about 103 volts.

RF Coils

Radio coils, also called inductors, inductances, couplers, or transformers, are used in resonant circuits for tuning selective filtering and in nonresonant circuits for filtering, as well as for signal loads.

A radio coil is usually a coil of wire wound on a tubular, insulated form with or without a powdered iron (ferrite) core. For use at very high and ultra high frequencies, it may consist of a piece of wire, straight or shaped like a hairpin. For use at very low frequencies, it may consist of thousands of turns of wire in layers.

The schematic symbols of several types of single winding coils were shown in Fig. 5. A fixed (nonadjustable) coil with an air core (wound on insulated tubing) was shown in Fig. 36. An arrow through a coil symbol indicates that the inductance of the coil is adjustable, but the specific adjustment technique is not defined. The coil shown in Fig. 37 is one with adjustable inductance by means of moving its ferrite core. Coil inductance is adjustable by selection of the number of active turns, either by a sliding contact or by tapped turns. Lines alongside a coil symbol indicate that the coil has a nonadjustable iron core.

When two or more coils are wound on the same form and placed in close proximity to each other, the device is a transformer (Fig. 38). When the symbol makes it appear that the primary and secondary have the same number of turns, this is not necessarily so.

Figure 39(A) shows an RF autotransformer schematically, a single coil with a tap. It can be used either as a stepup or stepdown transformer, depending on whether the entire coil is used as the primary or the secondary. The stepup or stepdown ratio depends on the location of the tap.

A three-winding RF transformer is shown in Fig. 40. Coil L1 could be the antenna coil, L2 the coil that drives the grid, and L3 the tickler or feedback coil when the transformer is used in a regenerative circuit.

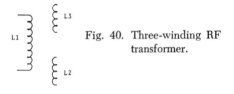

Fig. 40.   Three-winding RF transformer.

• CAPACITORS

Capacitors used to be called condensers; some people still use the older name. Next to the resistor, the capacitor is the most widely used electronic component. There are fixed and variable capacitors as well as capacitive transducers (condenser microphones for example).

Paper Capacitors

The most common type of capacitor is the paper tubular, such as the one shown in Fig. 41. They are available in numerous capacitance values, as Table 4 indicates. A paper tubular capacitor consists of two strips of metal foil insulated from each other by a strip of treated paper, the dielectric. The three-layer assembly is then rolled to form a tubular structure, which is covered by a cardboard tube or molded in an insulating material. Connection to each of the strips is made through wire leads, one at each end of the assembly.

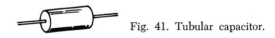

Fig. 41. Tubular capacitor.

Table 4

STANDARD PAPER CAPACITOR VALUES

(In microfarads)

.0001	.0025	.01	.04	.15
.00025	.003	.015	.047	.2
.0005	.004	.02	.05	.22
.001	.0047	.022	.06	.25
.0015	.005	.025	.068	.5
.002	.0068	.03	.1	1.0

Symbols

The schematic symbols for capacitors were shown previously in Fig. 5. The curved line, in the case of a paper tubular capacitor, represents the outer layer of foil. It is this side of the capacitor that should be connected to the grounded side of a circuit or to the part of the circuit that is least apt to pick up hum or noise.

Ratings

Other types of fixed capacitors include those employing mica or other insulating material as a dielectric. The capacity of a paper tubular capacitor is usually printed on its exterior. Mica and other molded capacitors are identified by the color code shown in Fig. 42.

Capacitors are also rated in terms of DC working voltage and test voltage. The working voltage is the highest DC voltage that should be applied to a capacitor in its circuit. To be on the safe side, use a capacitor with a rated working voltage higher than the voltage to be applied to it.

The amount of capacitance depends on the surface area of the electrodes and the thickness and characteristics of the dielectric.

Charging

When an electrical potential (voltage) is applied to the terminals of a capacitor, the capacitor becomes charged almost

CAPACITORS

Generally, only mica and tubular ceramic capacitors, used in modern equipment, are color coded. The color codes differ somewhat among capacitor manufacturers, however the codes shown below apply to practically all of the mica and tubular ceramic capacitors that are in common use. These codes comply with EIA (Electronics Industries Association) Standards.

MICA

CODE

COLOR	1st DIGIT	2nd DIGIT	MULTIPLIER	TOLER %
BLACK	0	0	1	±20
BROWN	1	1	10	
RED	2	2	100	±2
ORANGE	3	3	1,000	±3
YELLOW	4	4	10,000	
GREEN	5	5		±5
BLUE	6	6		
VIOLET	7	7		
GRAY	8	8		
WHITE	9	9		
GOLD			.1	
SILVER			.01	±10

OBSERVE DIRECTION OF ARROW

WHT OR BLK DOT INDICATES MICA

(VALUE IN μμf—SEE NOTE 3 BELOW)

EXAMPLE

2   7 x 100
RED VIOL RED

MICA   GRN ±5%

CHARACTERISTIC—SEE NOTE 1 BELOW

2,700 μμf ±5%
OR .0027 μfd

TUBULAR CERAMIC

Place the group of rings or dots to the left and read from left to right.

CODE

COLOR	1st DIGIT	2nd DIGIT	MULTIPLIER	TOLER % 10 OR LESS μμf	TOLER % OVER 10
BLACK	0	0	1	±2.0	±20
BROWN	1	1	10	±0.1	±1
RED	2	2	100		±2
ORANGE	3	3	1,000		±2.5
YELLOW	4	4	10,000		
GREEN	5	5		±0.5	±5
BLUE	6	6			
VIOLET	7	7			
GRAY	8	8		±0.25	
WHITE	9	9		±1.0	±10

TEMPERATURE COEFFICIENT—SEE NOTE 2 BELOW.

(VALUE IN μμf—SEE NOTE 3 BELOW)

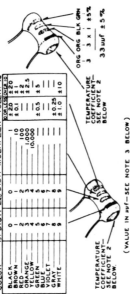

EXAMPLE

ORG ORG BLK GRN ±5%
3   3 x 1 ±5%

33 μμf ±5%

TEMPERATURE COEFFICIENT SEE NOTE 2 BELOW

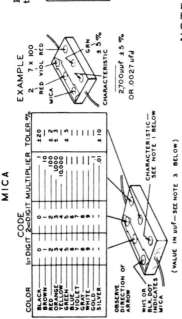

NOTES:

1. The characteristic of a mica capacitor is the temperature coefficient, drift capacitance and insulation resistance. This information is not usually needed to identify a capacitor but, if desired, it can be obtained by referring to EIA Standard, RS-153 (a Standard of Electronic Industries Association.)

2. The temperature coefficient of a capacitor is the predictable change in capacitance with temperature change and is expressed in parts per million per degree centigrade. Refer to EIA Standard, RS-198 (a Standard of Electronic Industries Association.)

3. The farad is the basic unit of capacitance, however capacitor values are generally expressed in terms of μfd (microfarad, .000001 farad) and μμf (micro-micro-farad, .000001 μfd); therefore, 1,000 μμf = .001 μfd, 1,000,000 μμf = 1 μfd. The designation pf is sometimes used for μμf.

Fig. 42. Capacitor color code (Courtesy of Heath Co.).

instantly to the same potential as the applied voltage. When the external voltage is disconnected, the capacitor remains charged until the charge leaks off slowly through the dielectric. The capacitor can be discharged instantly by short circuiting of its terminals.

A voltage doubler can be formed by charging two capacitors of identical capacity in parallel and then connecting them in series.

Time Constant

The charge and discharge time of a capacitor can be increased by connecting a resistor in series with it as shown in Fig. 43. When switch S is set to the "charge" position, capacitor C at first looks like a short circuit and maximum current flows through resistor R. As C becomes charged, current decreases and falls off to zero when C is fully charged.

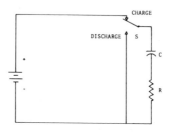

Fig. 43. Capacitor charge and discharge circuit.

When S is thrown to the "discharge" position, maximum current will again flow through R (but in the reverse direction) and taper off to zero as C discharges through R.

When the capacitor has a value of 1.0 mf (microfarad) and the resistor has a value of one megohm (one million ohms), the capacitor will charge to 63% of the supply voltage in one second. The time constant of the circuit is computed by $T = RC$, where T is time in seconds, R is resistance in megohms, and C is capacity in microfarads.

Reactance

DC does not flow through a capacitor (except electrolytic types) except when it is charging or discharging. AC flows through a capacitor, since it is alternately charged and discharged. The resistance of the flow of AC is known as inductive reactance, which is determined by the value of capacitance and the frequency of the AC. For example, the reactance of an 0.001-microfarad capacitor is about 270,000 ohms at 60 Hz (cps). The reactance of an 0.1-mf capacitor at the same frequency is one tenth as high. If the frequency of the AC is increased, the reactance is decreased. Thus, at RF, the reactance of an 0.01-mf capacitor is so low that it acts as a short circuit to the RF signal and as an open circuit to DC.

Electrolytic Capacitors

DC flows through an electrolytic capacitor (the schematic symbol was shown previously in Fig. 5). The curved line represents the negative terminal of an electrolytic capacitor, and the straight line represents the positive terminal.

An electrolytic capacitor is polarity-sensitive. When it is connected as shown in Fig. 44(A), a small amount of leakage current will flow. When it is connected as shown in Fig. 44(B), very high current will flow, and the capacitor may be destroyed.

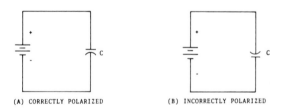

(A) CORRECTLY POLARIZED   (B) INCORRECTLY POLARIZED

Fig. 44. Electrolytic capacitors are polarity sensitive.

Electrolytic capacitors are commonly used in transistor circuits where high values of capacitance (low reactance) are

45

required. In such circuits, the capacitors are connected with consideration of polarity.

One of the most common applications of capacitors is in plate voltage power supplies as ripple filters. As in the case of conventional capacitors, working voltage ratings must not be exceeded. A new electrolytic capacitor may pass considerable leakage current, which falls off as the capacitor forms.

Fig. 45. Electrolytic capacitors connected in series opposing can be used in AC circuits.

Electrolytic capacitors can be used in AC circuits by connection of them in series opposing, as shown in Fig. 45. In this example, the capacitors are used to reduce the low frequency output of a loudspeaker. At high frequencies, the series reactance of the capacitors is low; at low frequencies, the reactance is high and reduces the amount of low frequency current flowing through the loudspeaker.

Variable Capacitors

In any capacitor, the value of capacitance depends on the surface areas of the electrodes with respect to each other, their spacing, and the dielectric. In a variable capacitor, capacity is varied by adjustment of the spacing between the electrodes or the relationship of the surface area of one electrode to that of the other.

A conventional variable tuning capacitor usually consists of a number of fixed plates (stator) connected to each other, and a number of movable plates (rotor) connected to each other (Fig. 46). When the rotor plates are fully meshed with the stator plates, capacity is maximum.

Capacitors of this type are often ganged to permit a simultaneous tuning of two or more circuits with a single dial.

46

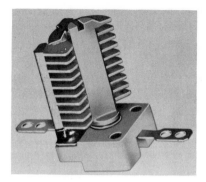

Fig. 46. Variable capacitor.

Fig. 47. Trimmer capacitor.

Other types of variable capacitors, which are usually adjusted with a screwdriver or tuning wrench, are known as trimmer or padder capacitors (Fig. 47). A compression-type capacitor usually employs metal electrodes separated by mica. Tightening of the adjusting screw applies greater compression, increasing the capacitance. Various other types of trimmers are also used, such as miniature versions of air-dielectric tuning capacitors and piston types.

• L-C CIRCUITS

A coil or transformer is never purely inductive. Its winding or windings are also resistive because the wire does not have zero resistance. It also has some capacitance, since adjacent turns act as the electrodes of a capacitor.

Self-resonance

A coil by itself is resonant at the frequency at which its inductive reactance and capacitive reactance are equal. This is known as "self-resonance." If the coil has an adjustable ferrite core with which its inductance can be varied, the frequency of self-resonance can be adjusted. At the resonant frequency, the impedance (AC resistance) of the coil is maximum.

Parallel Resonance

When a coil and a capacitor are connected in parallel, their impedance is extremely high at the frequency at which their reactances are equal. At that frequency only, the circuit is said to be parallel-resonant. Such circuits are used in most tuned stages of frequency-selective amplifiers and radio transmitters and receivers. When such circuits are connected in series with a radio antenna, as in Fig. 48, a parallel-resonant wave-trap is formed that blocks passage of signals at the

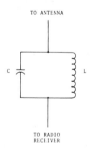

Fig. 48. Parallel-resonant wave trap.

frequency at which the circuit is resonant. It passes signals at other frequencies because of the low reactance of the capacitor at higher frequencies and the low reactance of the coil at lower frequencies. This effect is not canceled out by the inductive reactance. In the above circuits, either the capacitor or the coil, or both can be variable. The inductance of a coil may be varied by means of taps on its winding and selection of the number of active turns with a switch or with movement of its core within the winding, if it is a radio coil with an adjustable core.

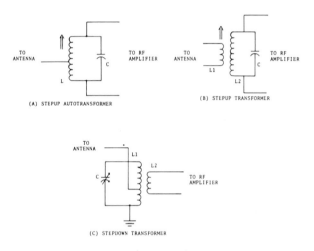

Fig. 49. RF transformer.

Radio tuning and other adjustable resonant circuits are shown symbolically in Fig. 49. Part A could represent the antenna coil of a fixed-tuned radio communications receiver, which, in this case, is an autotransformer. The antenna is connected to the tap. The capacitor across the entire coil is fixed, and the circuit is tuned by adjustment of the ferrite core to change the value of inductance. However, the coil could be fixed and the capacitor adjustable.

In Part B, the coil at the left could be the antenna coil. This configuration is often used in lieu of the one shown in Part A to permit connection of a low impedance antenna to a high impedance resonant circuit.

In a transistor radio receiver, a coil arrangement such as that shown in Part C is sometimes used. The primary is a tunable resonant circuit with a low impedance antenna tap, coupled to a low impedance secondary, which feeds the low resistance input of a transistor.

Most radio IF (intermediate frequency) transformers employ two identical coils inductively coupled to each other. Both coils are tuned to the same frequency by means of a variable capacitor across each of the coils, as shown in Part A of Fig. 50, or with an adjustable ferrite core within each coil, as in Part B. The symbol C is sometimes used to represent the same thing as B.

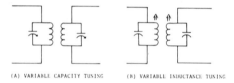

(A) VARIABLE CAPACITY TUNING   (B) VARIABLE INDUCTANCE TUNING

Fig. 50. Double-tuned RF/IF transformers.

Q Factor

It is often assumed that an IF transformer provides no gain, since it is a 1:1 transformer (same number of turns on primary and secondary). This is not necessarily so. It can provide gain or introduce loss, depending on coupling and the "Q" (merit of the coils). It has been explained that the primary functions as a parallel-resonant circuit and the secondary as a series-resonant circuit.

Signals at the resonant frequency encounter an extremely high impedance load, and a high signal voltage is developed across the primary. Relatively high current flows through the primary, creating an intense magnetic field that permeates the secondary.

Some theorists postulate that the energy from the primary is actually induced into the secondary circuit as if it were applied at "X" in Fig. 51. At the resonant frequency, the voltages across the secondary and its associated capacitor are high, but out of phase with each other. The voltage across each could be considerably higher than the primary voltage. With application of the voltage across C2 to the input of the next stage, gain would be realized. However, the amount of gain (if any) would depend on the "Q" of the tuned circuits; thus, in actuality, gain may not be realized. It is an interesting concept, nevertheless.

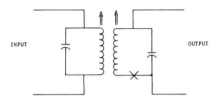

Fig. 51. Secondary of tuned transformer functions as a series-resonant circuit.

Series Resonance

Series resonance was involved above in reference to Fig. 51, although schematically a parallel-resonant circuit was shown. When a coil and a capacitor are connected in series, as shown in Fig. 52, series resonance occurs at the frequency at which the inductive and capacitive reactances are equal. The impedance (AC resistance) of the series-resonant circuit (L and C) will be minimum (close to zero). In the circuit shown, the lamp will glow brightly when the circuit is resonant. If the frequency of the applied voltage is changed, or if the value of inductance or capacitance is changed, the impedance will rise sharply.

At resonance, the voltage across the coil or capacitor individually could be considerably higher than the supply voltage.

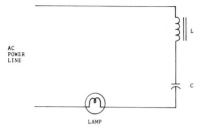

AC
POWER
LINE

L

C

LAMP

Fig. 52. Series-resonant circuit.

But the voltage across both of them collectively could be close
to zero, since their individual voltages are in phase opposition
to each other.

Nonresonant Circuits

Coils are used as nonresonant loads, as shown in Fig. 53.
In Part A, the coil has considerable inductance and is self-
resonant at a frequency much lower than the operating frequency of the device in which it is used. In Part B, an iron

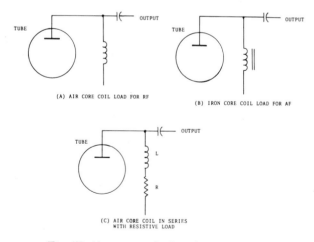

TUBE   OUTPUT

(A) AIR CORE COIL LOAD FOR RF

TUBE   OUTPUT

(B) IRON CORE COIL LOAD FOR AF

TUBE   OUTPUT

L

R

(C) AIR CORE COIL IN SERIES
WITH RESISTIVE LOAD

Fig. 53. Nonresonant load applications of coils.

core coil (AF choke) is used as the plate load in an AF amplifier stage. And, in Part C, an air core coil is used to improve the high frequency response of the amplifier. Resistor R is assumed to be insensitive to frequency. At low frequencies, the reactance of the coil is small, and very little voltage is developed across it. But at high frequencies, its reactance is large, and considerable signal voltage is developed across it. Thus, the voltage fed to the next stage is higher, since the voltages across L and R are in series.

When a coil symbol is labeled "RFC," it means that it is a radio frequency choke (Fig. 54), a coil which readily passes DC and AF, but blocks passage of RF. There are many uses for RF chokes. As shown in Fig. 55, an RF choke permits passage of DC and AF to the plate of the RF power amplifier of a transmitter without short circuiting the RF to ground because of its high reactance at radio frequencies.

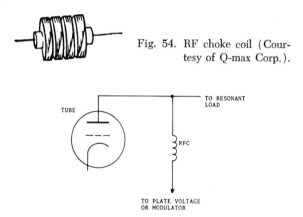

Fig. 54. RF choke coil (Courtesy of Q-max Corp.).

Fig. 55. RF choke as signal isolator.

RF chokes are also used in power line filters, as shown in Fig. 56. Power line current (60 Hz) readily flows through the chokes, but passage of noise at radio frequencies and radio signals is blocked.

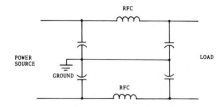

Fig. 56. Power line interference filter.

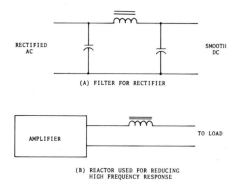

Fig. 57. Applications of iron core reactors.

Iron core AF and filter chokes have considerable inductance and are used to pass DC and restrict the flow of AC, as well as to alter audio frequency response. In Part A of Fig. 57, a choke is used in a plate voltage power supply to provide a high reactance path to the 60 Hz ripple, without causing a large DC voltage-drop. In Part B, a choke is used to reduce the high frequency output of an amplifier. At low frequencies, the choke has relatively low reactance; but at high frequencies, its reactance is much greater, and current flow through the load is smaller at high frequencies than at low frequencies.

4 : Diodes

A diode is a two-electrode device that readily passes current in one direction and resists or blocks current flow in the other direction. A diode may be a solid state semiconductor device or a thermionic device (tube). The most common application of a diode is as a rectifier. Diodes are also used as voltage-controlled gates and switches, as well as voltage regulators.

• SEMICONDUCTORS

The earliest diode was a crystal detector, a hunk of galena or silicon. It was the heart of early crystal radio receiving sets using a circuit such as the one shown in Fig. 58. Contact to the crystal (CR) was made through its metal holder and a springy wire known as a cat whisker. Today, crystal sets use what is known as a semiconductor diode employing germanium or silicon.

Characteristics

A diode has many applications besides that as a radio detector. But first, the characteristics of semiconductor diodes

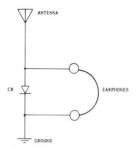

Fig. 58. The first application
of diodes was in crys-
tal radio receivers.

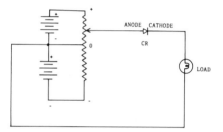

Fig. 59. Circuit for demonstrating operation of a diode.

must be discussed. If we use the circuit shown in Fig. 59, we can determine what takes place. When the potentiometer is set as shown in the diagram, diode CR is forward biased, since its anode is positive with respect to its cathode. Current flows through the lamp load. The lamp gets brighter as the potentiometer is adjusted to make the voltage more positive, and vice versa.

If the potentiometer is set to the zero (0) voltage point, obviously no current flows. As the potentiometer is adjusted to apply a small positive voltage, no current flows until the potential across the diode exceeds its barrier voltage (about 300 millivolts). When the potentiometer is adjusted to increase the voltage beyond the barrier, the forward resistance of the diode drops almost to zero, and the current level is determined by the lamp resistance and the applied voltage level. Hence, the diode is a variable resistance that is high below its barrier voltage and extremely low at higher voltages.

Now, if the potentiometer is adjusted past the zero point to apply negative voltage, the diode is reverse biased. No current flows except a very minute leakage current. If the potentiometer is adjusted to make the voltage sufficiently negative, heavy current flows because the diode avalanches. This is known as the Zener effect. Some diodes can be destroyed by excessive reverse current; others are designed to be used in this manner.

Amplitude Limiters

The diode barrier can be used in an amplitude limiter circuit, as shown in Fig. 60. Here, two diodes are connected in parallel, but in opposing polarity, across the AC signal, which is applied through series resistance R.

Fig. 60. Simple amplitude limiter.

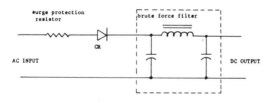

Fig. 61. Half-wave rectifier power supply with L-C filter.

When the input signal is very small (below 300 millivolts), both diodes act as very high resistances, and the output voltage is almost the same as the input voltage. But when the input signal level rises and swings toward positive, diode CR1 conducts and acts as a very low resistance across the output. There is a large voltage-drop across R because of the current flow through CR1. When the input signal swings to negative, CR1 stops conducting and CR2 conducts, applying a low resistance across the output. Hence, the output signal cannot rise much higher than the barrier voltage of the diodes.

Rectifiers

One of the most common applications of a diode (Fig. 61) is as a rectifier in a power supply. For example, one inexpensive diode (CR) is used in the half-wave rectifier circuit shown in Fig. 62. Resistor R1 (only a few ohms) is sometimes used to protect the diode when the forward current is very high while C1 is charging. The pulsating DC is filtered by C1, C2, and R2.

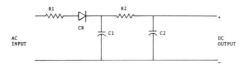

Fig. 62. Half-wave rectifier employing a semiconductor diode.

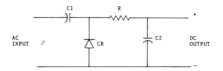

Fig. 63. Half-wave shunt rectifier.

A diode can be used as a shunt rectifier, as shown in Fig. 63. Here, the diode acts as an open circuit (reverse biased) when the AC voltage applied through C1 is positive, and as a short circuit when the input voltage polarity reverses. During the time the diode acts as a short circuit, the current

58

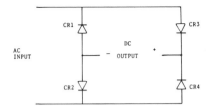

Fig. 64. Full-wave bridge rectifier.

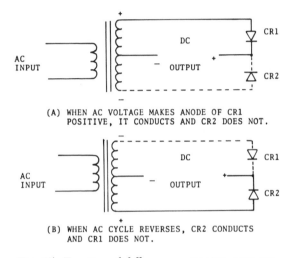

(A) WHEN AC VOLTAGE MAKES ANODE OF CR1
POSITIVE, IT CONDUCTS AND CR2 DOES NOT.

(B) WHEN AC CYCLE REVERSES, CR2 CONDUCTS
AND CR1 DOES NOT.

Fig. 65. Function of full-wave, center-tap type rectifier.

through the diode is limited to the current required to charge
C1.

With the use of four diodes in a bridge rectifier circuit, as
shown in Fig. 64, full-wave rectification is obtained. Diodes
CR1 and CR2 conduct during one half of the cycle, and CR3
and CR4 during the other half-cycle. Only two diodes are
required for full-wave rectification when a center-tapped
transformer is used, as shown in Fig. 65.

Voltage Doublers

Diodes are used in full-wave voltage-doubler rectifier circuits such as those shown in Fig. 66. Unlike these circuits, a half-wave voltage-doubler circuit, shown in Fig. 67, has the advantage that a transformer does not have to be used, since the negative leg is common ground.

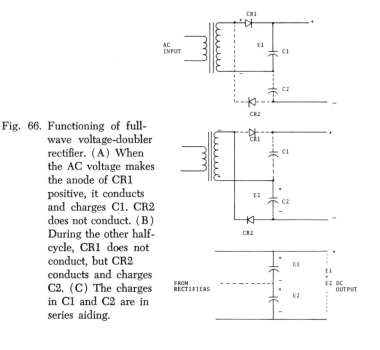

Fig. 66. Functioning of full-wave voltage-doubler rectifier. (A) When the AC voltage makes the anode of CR1 positive, it conducts and charges C1. CR2 does not conduct. (B) During the other half-cycle, CR1 does not conduct, but CR2 conducts and charges C2. (C) The charges in C1 and C2 are in series aiding.

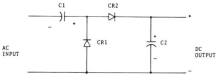

Fig. 67. Half-wave voltage-doubler. Charges in C1 and C2 are in series aiding.

Ratings

Diodes have many other applications, particularly in computer logic circuits. They are made by the millions in thousands of different types. Some can handle only a few milliamperes of forward current; others can handle several amperes. Diodes are rated in terms of forward current capacity and peak inverse voltage (PIV) or peak reverse voltage (PRV). The PIV or PRV is the maximum reverse bias that can be applied without destruction of the diode.

Zener Diodes

The Zener diode is widely used as a voltage regulator and voltage reference. Its reverse current is small when the voltage across it is less than its breakdown or avalanche voltage. When this voltage is attained, the reverse current becomes large and varies with the applied voltage. The voltage-drop across the diode, however, remains relatively constant. In Fig. 68, the DC input voltage can be varied with potentiometer R1. When R1 is adjusted to increase the voltage, the milliammeter (A) indicates very low current until the breakdown voltage is reached.

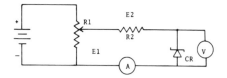

Fig. 68. Circuit for demonstrating characteristics of a Zener diode.

The voltmeter (V) indicates the level of the voltage as determined by the setting of R1 until the voltage is increased beyond the breakdown value. Further increase in voltage from R1 will cause no significant increase in voltmeter reading (voltage across Zener diode CR), but the ammeter reading will increase (current through diode).

61

The voltage drop across ballast resistor R2 varies with diode current. Hence, the voltage across the diode, as indicated by the voltmeter, is equal to the supply voltage (E1) minus the voltage-drop (E2) across R2.

The breakdown voltage of a Zener diode can be less than one volt or several hundred volts, depending on the diode. Often, two or more low voltage Zener diodes can be connected in series to provide regulated voltage at a desired value.

Tunnel Diodes

Tunnel diodes are used in industrial equipment. A tunnel (Esaki) diode, unlike a conventional diode or Zener diode, conducts heavily when reverse biased, even with a low voltage. When it is forward biased, current flow through a tunnel diode rises sharply, and then falls off as forward bias voltage is increased. Its resistance becomes negative, and current conduction is very small until the forward bias is increased further. Figure 69 shows the characteristic curve of a tunnel diode. The region of low current, when the diode is forward biased, is known as the valley. Tunnel diodes are used in computer logic circuits, as oscillators, and as FM detectors.

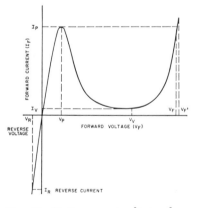

Fig. 69. Static current-voltage characteristics of a tunnel diode (Courtesy of Radio Corporation of America).

Varactor Diodes

Varactor diodes are now widely used as frequency multipliers and frequency modulators. A varactor diode acts as a capacitor the capacity of which can be changed by varying the voltage applied to it.

Light-sensitive Diodes

Other types of diodes include those that are light sensitive. Their conductivity (resistance) varies with the light applied. Some are capable of conducting considerable current, and unlike tube-type photoelectric cells, they can be used without an amplifier in a circuit, such as shown in Fig. 70.

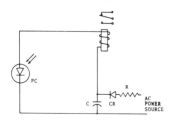

Fig. 70. Relay control circuit employing a light-sensitive diode.

Here, a photosensitive diode (PC) is used to control a relay. DC, required for the relay (R), is obtained by rectification of power line AC with diode CR and smoothing of the DC by filtering with capacitor C. Relay current is controlled by the amount of light reaching PC. When sufficient light reaches PC, its resistance decreases and the relay is energized.

• THERMIONIC DIODES

A long time ago, Thomas Edison, when working with his lamp, discovered that with placement of a metal plate against the glass bulb of a lamp, current would flow between the lamp filament and the plate. Later, an Englishman named Fleming used the "Edison effect" and created the Fleming valve, which is now known as a diode.

Diode Tubes

The British refer to a tube as a valve, since it actually is a valve. In Fig. 71 we have a schematic diagram of a diode tube the plate of which (sometimes called anode) is made positive with respect to its filament (properly called cathode) by battery B. The filament of the tube is heated by battery A.

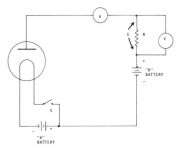

Fig. 71. Circuit for demonstrating characteristics
of a thermionic diode.

When switch S is open, there is no current flow through the load, resistor R, since the cathode is cold. When S is closed, the cathode temperature rises and electrons are emitted from it. Current now flows through R and between the plate and cathode, because the electrons emitted by the hot cathode are attracted to the positively charged plate. Hence, there is an electron flow between the plate and cathode that closes the circuit through the load resistor.

If we connect a voltmeter (V) across R and a milliammeter (A) in series with it, the milliammeter will indicate the level of the current through R and the tube. This is the plate current. The voltmeter will indicate the amount of voltage-drop across the load resistor caused by the current flowing through it. The level of the plate current depends on the voltage of the

B battery and the value of R, as well as the plate resistance of the diode.

Across the plate and cathode of the tube, there is a voltage-drop which is determined by the conductivity of the electron stream. The plate resistance depends on the distance between the plate and cathode, the temperature of the cathode, and the kind of material used for the cathode. The higher the cathode temperature, the greater the plate current and the lower the drop across the tube.

If the B battery potential is 90 volts, R has a value of 10,000 ohms, and the plate resistance of the diode is 2,000 ohms, then the plate current will be equal to 90 divided by 12,000 (the sum of the two resistances) or 0.0075 ampere (7.5 milliamperes). The sum of the voltage-drops across the tube and the load resistance must equal the B battery voltage.

The voltage drop across R is 75 volts, since E is equal to IR or 0.0075 times 10,000. The voltage-drop across the tube is 15 volts, since 0.0075 times 2,000 equals 15. The sum of 75 and 15 is, of course, 90.

Now, if we reverse the polarity of the B battery, the plate is negative with respect to the cathode, and there will be no electron flow from the cathode to the plate. There is no plate current or voltage-drop across R. We now have an open switch; hence, a diode is a polarity-sensitive valve.

Although the schematic symbol shows the plate as being at one side of the cathode (filament), in a real diode the plate is usually a metal cylinder surrounding, but not touching, the cathode.

The circuit in Fig. 71 shows a filament-type diode employing a filament that is a directly heated cathode. Most tubes have an indirectly heated cathode. There is a filament, but it is known as a heater. It is surrounded by the cathode, but is electrically insulated from it. The cathode is coated with a material that emits an abundance of electrons when its temperature is raised by the heater. The heater itself is not supposed to emit electrons. Figure 72 illustrates schematically the difference between filament-type and heater-type tubes.

Fig. 72. Directly and indirectly heated cathodes.

Heater Voltage

So far, it has been seen that plate current depends on cathode temperature, tube plate resistance, load resistance, and plate supply voltage. Hence, in an auto radio or two-way mobile radio unit, the tubes draw more plate current when the engine is running, because higher voltage is applied from the car battery and generator. This increases the heater temperatures because of a rise in heater voltage (A battery). The plate supply voltage from the power supply (equivalent of a B battery) of the set also rises.

Tubes, however, are designed to operate longer when the heater voltage is not increased above rated values. For example, a 6.3-volt tube should be operated at within $+5\%$ of 6.3 volts. This voltage is sometimes exceeded, but such excess is not harmful if not of long duration. On the other hand, a tube operated considerably below its rated voltage may last very long, but not provide its intended performance.

There are also limitations on plate voltage and current as well as on the voltage difference between cathode and heater. This information for specific tube types can be found in tube directories.

For the sake of simplicity, the heater is not shown in many schematic diagrams. In Fig. 73(A), an actual circuit of a heater-type diode is shown, revealing that AC is applied to its heater from a transformer winding. In Fig. 73(B), the heater circuit is not shown, but H1 and H2 at the low voltage transformer winding indicate that these leads go to the heater.

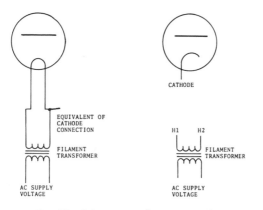

EQUIVALENT OF
CATHODE
CONNECTION

FILAMENT
TRANSFORMER

AC SUPPLY
VOLTAGE

CATHODE

H1   H2

FILAMENT
TRANSFORMER

AC SUPPLY
VOLTAGE

Fig. 73. Schematic diagram techniques for showing filament and heater connections. (A) Filament diode. (B) Cathode-type diode (heater not shown).

Half-wave Rectifiers

In Fig. 74, a diode tube (V) is used as a half-wave rectifier. The voltage across the transformer secondary leads, labeled P1 and P2, changes its polarity at the applied AC voltage frequency (usually 60 times per second). When P1 is positive and P2 is negative, the plate of the diode is positive with respect to its cathode. The diode is forward biased and, there-

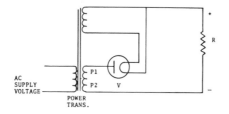

AC
SUPPLY
VOLTAGE

P1
P2   V

POWER
TRANS.

R

Fig. 74. Half-wave rectifier employing thermionic diode.

fore, conducts. There is a voltage-drop across R, since plate current flows.

When the AC supply voltage reverses polarity (P1 negative and P2 positive), the plate is negative with respect to the cathode. The diode is now reverse biased and cannot conduct. Hence, no current flows through R.

However, if a DC voltmeter is connected across R, it will indicate the presence of DC voltage. Current flows through R intermittently, and its level varies with the applied AC voltage sine wave, as shown in Fig. 75(B). Even though there is voltage present less than half of the time (no voltage between voltage pulses), the meter indicates voltage, because its mechanism is not fast enough to follow the voltage changes.

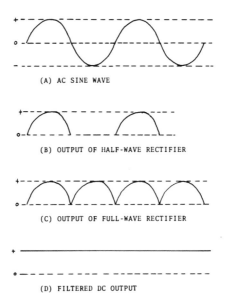

(A) AC SINE WAVE

(B) OUTPUT OF HALF-WAVE RECTIFIER

(C) OUTPUT OF FULL-WAVE RECTIFIER

(D) FILTERED DC OUTPUT

Fig. 75. Power supply wave forms.

Filters

To make use of this pulsating DC voltage in electronics applications, it is necessary to filter it. This can be done by connecting a large capacitor across the load. The capacitor charges to the peak value of the AC voltage (1.4 times the RMS value) less the voltage-drop across the tube. During the periods when the diode is reverse biased, the capacitor retains the charge and sustains the voltage across R, so that it becomes a steady DC voltage, as shown in Fig. 75(D).

The quality of the DC voltage depends on the size of the capacitor and the value of R. If the load current (R represents the load) is increased, the DC voltage drops because of a rise in forward voltage-drop across the tube and, possibly, because of a capacitor of insufficient size.

Full-wave Rectifiers

By adding a second diode (using a duo-diode rectifier tube), one can form a full-wave rectifier, as shown in Fig. 76, using a center-tapped transformer secondary. When P1 is positive and P3 is negative, one half of diode V conducts, since it is forward biased, but the other half does not conduct, since it is reverse biased. Since current flows through R, a DC voltage is developed across it. When P1 becomes negative and P2 becomes positive, the previously reverse-biased diode con-

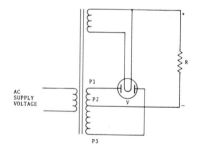

Fig. 76. Full-wave rectifier
employing duo-diode
rectifier tube.

ducts. Current flows through R in the same direction as before, and rises and falls as shown in Fig. 75(C), but without the gaps present with a half-wave rectifier.

With connection of a capacitor across R, the DC voltage across it can be made steady. The pulsations of voltage, when not adequately filtered, are known as ripple. Under operation from a 60 Hz AC source, the ripple frequency of a half-wave rectifier is 60 Hz, and that of a full-wave rectifier is 120 Hz because of the push-push action.

Another kind of full-wave rectifier circuit is shown in Fig. 77. Two cathode-type, duo-diode tubes are used. This is a bridge rectifier that does not require a center-tapped transformer. When P1 is positive and P2 is negative, diodes V1A and V2A are forward biased and allow current to pass through R; but V1B and V2B are reverse biased and do not conduct. When the AC voltage reverses its polarity, V1B and V2B conduct, and V1A and V2A do not conduct. Hence, current flows through R to reduce or eliminate the ripple and to increase the level of the DC voltage.

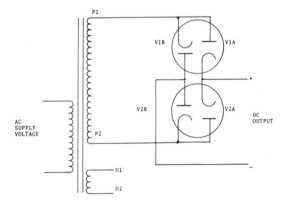

Fig. 77. Full-wave bridge rectifier employing two cathode-type, duo-diode tubes.

Voltage Doublers

One of the most commonly used circuits is the voltage doubler. Two diodes (in one tube envelope) are used, as shown in Fig. 78. When P1 is positive and P2 is negative, diode V1 conducts and charges capacitor C1 to the peak value of the AC voltage. When the AC voltage polarity reverses, V2 conducts and charges C2. Since C1 and C2 are connected with their charges in series aiding, the voltage across R is approximately twice the AC peak voltage across P1–P2. For example, if the P1–P2 voltage is 100 volts RMS, the DC voltage across C1 will be approximately 140 volts, and 140 volts will be developed across C2. Therefore, the voltage across R should be approximately 280 volts, depending on load current and the size of the capacitors. The ripple frequency will be 120 Hz, since this is a full-wave circuit.

The diodes covered so far are vacuum tubes with hot cathodes. There are also gas tube diodes with hot or cold cathodes. But the most popular type of diode used today is the semiconductor diode, which was discussed earlier in this chapter.

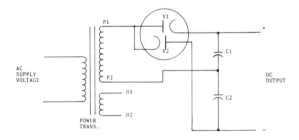

Fig. 78. Full-wave voltage doubler with duo-diode rectifier tube.

5 : Tubes

The diode became a triode when Dr. Lee De Forest in 1906 added a third element, the grid, between the cathode and the plate. A thermionic diode, as discussed previously, functions as a directional resistor in an electrical circuit. The amount of resistance inserted into the circuit by the diode remains constant as long as the values of the other circuit components do not change. The diode's conductivity, which determines its resistance, could be varied by changing the cathode temperature of the diode.

• TRIODES

The Grid

There is a much better way to control electron flow from cathode to plate. A grid can be inserted between cathode and plate. It usually is a wire mesh surrounding the cathode. A grid acts as a brake which can be used to reduce or completely stop electron flow from the cathode to the plate. In Fig. 79, for example, electrons flow past the grid to the plate, causing current to flow through load resistor R2, but only when switch S is in the "go" position (contacts closed).

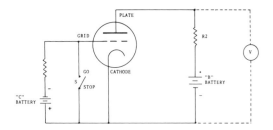

Fig. 79. Circuit for demonstrating effect of the
grid in a triode tube.

Electronic Gate

When the switch is set at the "stop" position (contacts open), a relatively high negative voltage is applied to the grid by the S battery. The negatively charged electrons are repelled by the negatively charged grid and cannot reach the plate.

If a DC voltmeter (V) is connected to the circuit, as shown in the diagram, it will indicate the full plate supply voltage when S is in the "stop" position, since the tube is in the so-called cut-off state. When S is in the "go" position, the grid-to-cathode voltage is zero, and the grid does not impede the flow of electrons. The meter will indicate a lower voltage because of plate current flow.

The cathode-to-plate resistance is made infinitely high when the grid is made sufficiently negative with respect to the cathode, so as to cut off plate current (electron flow). When the negative grid voltage is removed, the cathode-to-plate resistance is reduced, but never to zero. If it could be reduced to zero, the voltmeter would indicate zero, since all of the plate supply voltage would be dropped across R2.

Here, we are assuming that the voltmeter has infinite resistance, which is never the case. Batteries are shown as voltage sources in the diagrams for the sake of easy explanation.

Electronically Variable Resistance

It has been shown that a triode tube, called the Audion by

73

De Forest, functions as a variable resistance. In Fig. 79, the resistance is changed from infinity to a fairly low value (several thousand ohms). In Fig. 80, the grid voltage can be varied from zero to the full output voltage of the C battery.

As potentiometer R1 is turned to increase the negative voltage on the grid (with respect to the cathode), the electron flow is reduced. The plate current flowing through R2 is reduced, and the plate-to-cathode voltage rises (indicated by the voltmeter). Note that as the grid becomes more negative, the plate becomes more positive. As the negative grid voltage is reduced, it becomes less negative (positive going), and the plate voltage becomes less positive (negative going). Hence the triode inverts the phase of the applied voltage (to the grid) by 180 degrees.

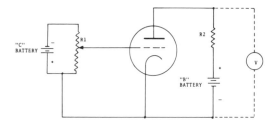

Fig. 80. Simple DC amplifier.

Amplification

The plate resistance of the tube is varied by changing the grid voltage. In Fig. 80, the plate-to-cathode resistance of the triode changes as the grid voltage changes, causing the plate current through R2 to change. A small change in grid voltage causes a large change in plate voltage. Hence, there is amplification. If a 1-volt change in grid voltage causes a 10-volt change in plate voltage (as indicated by the voltmeter), the input signal is amplified 10 times (20 db). A triode is known as a voltage amplifier. In the circuits shown, a triode is used as a DC amplifier, in Fig. 79 as an electronic

74

switch or digital amplifier, and in Fig. 80 as an analog amplifier.

AC Amplifier

A triode can also be used as an AC amplifier, as shown in Fig. 81. Here, a small AC voltage, obtained from transformer T, is fed to the grid in series with an adjustable DC voltage from the C battery. The purpose of the C battery is to bias the grid. By adjustment of potentiometer R1, the grid bias can be set to a value which will cause the triode to operate as a linear amplifier.

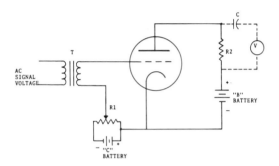

Fig. 81. Simple AC amplifier.

When the AC voltage reverses polarity, it is in series aiding series opposition to the DC bias voltage and reduces the net grid voltage (makes it less negative). This causes the plate current to rise and the plate voltage to fall, because of the increase in voltage drop across R2.

When the AC voltage applied to the grid is positive, it is in with the DC bias voltage and increases the net grid voltage (makes it more negative). This causes plate current to fall and the plate voltage to rise. When the bias voltage is correctly adjusted, the rise and fall of plate voltage with AC input voltage polarity reversals will be of the same magnitude.

Effects of Bias

However, if the bias voltage is sufficiently increased (grid

75

more negative), the negative excursions of the AC input signal will cause the tube to cut off. At some point, plate current will cease flowing, and plate voltage will not rise further. Positive AC signal excursions, on the other hand, will have a greater effect on plate current. Hence, the AC signal across R2, which can be measured with an AC voltmeter (V), as shown in the diagram, will not have the same waveform as the AC input signal. Capacitor C in the diagram passes the AC signal, but keeps the DC plate voltage out of the AC voltmeter.

On the other hand, if the grid bias is reduced below a certain value (with R1), a positive excursion of the AC input voltage (if large enough) will cause the tube to saturate. At saturation, plate current cannot be increased. A negative AC signal excursion will cause a sharp reduction in plate current. Hence, the output signal waveform will not be a facsimile of the input signal waveform.

In most applications, a triode is operated as a Class A amplifier. The bias is set so that the output signal is a magnified reproduction of the input signal. When a triode is operated as a Class B amplifier, the grid is biased more negatively than for Class A operation, so that positive-going input signals have a greater effect on plate current than negative-going input signals. In a Class C amplifier, the grid is biased so far negative that no plate current flows, except during the peaks of positive input signals.

Fixed Bias

When the bias voltage is derived from a battery, voltage divider, or rectifier, the amplifier is said to have fixed bias. In Fig. 81, fixed bias is furnished by the C battery. In Fig. 82 is shown a resistance-coupled amplifier stage. The AC input signal is fed through capacitor C1 to the grid and from the plate, through capacitor C2, to the next stage. An AC voltmeter (V) is shown here to indicate that an AC voltage is present at the output when an AC signal is present at the input.

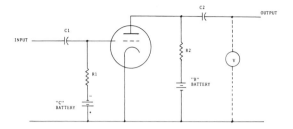

Fig. 82. Resistance-coupled amplifier with fixed bias.

Resistor R1 provides a path for the DC bias voltage and acts as a load for the AC input signal.

Cathode Bias

Fixed bias is not used as often as cathode bias. A negative DC voltage can be derived, for use as the bias voltage, by insertion of a resistor (R3) in series with the cathode, as shown in Fig. 83. When no AC input signal is present, cathode-to-plate current flows through both R3 and R2. Since they are in series, the same amount of current flows through both. If, for example, the plate current is 1 milliampere (0.001 amp) and R3 has a value of 1,000 ohms, there will be a drop of 1 volt across R3. The voltage will be polarized as shown in the diagram.

The grid bias voltage is the voltage difference between grid and cathode. Here, the cathode is one volt positive with respect to the grid, making the grid one volt negative with respect

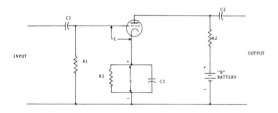

Fig. 83. Resistance-coupled amplifier with cathode bias.

to the cathode. The grid is connected through R1 to the negative end of R3. The cathode resistor (R3) is usually shunted
by a bypass capacitor (C3). When an AC signal is applied
to the grid, the voltage across R3 would also be AC if it were
not for the capacitor. When C3 is sufficiently large, rapid
current variations through R3 are prevented, and a near-pure
DC voltage is developed across R3.

Plate Load

The load resistor may be in either the plate or cathode
circuit. In Fig. 84, the load resistor is in series with the cathode. The plate is connected directly to the plate voltage source.
When the DC voltage applied to the grid is made more negative by adjustment of R1, current through R2 is reduced. The
voltage at the cathode, which is positive with respect to the
common ground buss, is reduced. This voltage is said to be
negative going (less positive).

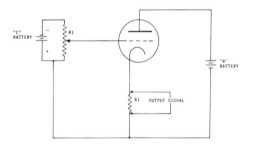

Fig. 84. DC amplifier with load in cathode
circuit.

A negative-going (more negative) input signal produces a
negative-going (less positive) output signal, and a positive-
going (less negative) input signal produces a positive-going
(more positive) output signal. Hence, the input and output
signals are in phase, whereas in a plate-loaded circuit, such
as shown previously in Fig. 83, they are 180 degrees out of
phase.

78

Cathode Follower

The circuit shown in Fig. 85 is that of an AC cathode follower with input and output signals in phase. Resistor R2 functions as both the cathode bias source and the output load. When there is no AC input signal, a DC voltage is developed across R2, which biases the grid. When the AC input signal swings positive, current through R2 increases, causing the output voltage, as measured by the AC voltmeter (V), to rise. However, the bias voltage also increases at the same time. Thus, the increase in current flow through R2 is inhibited. A negative-going AC input signal decreases current flow through R2, causing the output signal to fall off. But at the same time, the bias voltage is decreased. Therefore, the output signal is a replica of the input signal, but without amplification. A cathode follower, however, has a much lower ouput impedance than a plate-loaded amplifier and is often used as an interface between high impedance and low impedance circuits.

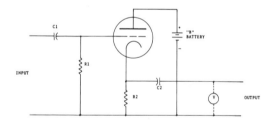

Fig. 85. Cathode-follower amplifier.

Transformer Coupling

A resistance has been shown as the output load in the circuits described so far. In Fig. 86, a transformer is used. A transformer is also used at the input. When there is no AC input signal, plate current is steady and is determined by the grid bias voltage, the plate supply voltage, and the DC resistance of the primary winding of T2.

79

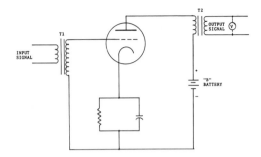

Fig. 86. Transformer-coupled AC amplifier.

When an AC input signal is applied to the grid, the plate current follows the AC input voltage variations. With respect to the AC signal, the impedance of the primary of T2 is large, although its resistance to DC is small. The variations in current flowing through it cause the development of a varying magnetic field that induces an AC voltage into the secondary. The output voltage, as measured by the AC voltmeter (V), is higher or lower than the voltage across the primary of T2, depending on whether T2 is a stepup or a stepdown transformer, respectively.

If the AC input voltage applied to the primary of T1 is 1 volt and T1 has a stepup ratio of 1:2, the grid will receive a 2-volt signal. If the tube provides 20 db of gain (10 times), a 20-volt signal will appear across the primary of T2. If T2 has a stepdown ratio of 20:1, the output signal will have a level of 1 volt. The voltage gain of the amplifier will be only one, or unity. However, there will be a power gain of 20 db (100 times) less some small loss in the transformers. The output power will be almost 100 times greater than the input power, even if the input and output voltages are the same. The input, obviously, is at a higher impedance than the ouput.

On the other hand, if T2 has a 1:2 stepup ratio, the output voltage will be 40 volts. The overall voltage gain will thus be 40 times. But, the power gain in db will remain the same, since the input and output impedances are not the same. A

80

transformer does not provide gain, but it can provide voltage stepup to stepdown with a small loss in power.

Inductive Load

An inductor, which is also called a reactor or choke, can be used as the plate load (R2) in a circuit such as the one shown in Fig. 83. Like the primary of T2 in Fig. 86, L serves as a high impedance load for AC signals, although its DC resistance may be low.

Resonant Load

The plate load of the amplifier circuit shown in Fig. 87 is tuned. At one frequency, L and C3 form a parallel resonant circuit. Gain is maximum at that frequency, since the impedance of the resonant circuit (LC) is at maximum. At all other frequencies, the gain is less. This kind of circuit is used in radio equipment and in tone decoders when amplification at only one frequency is desired.

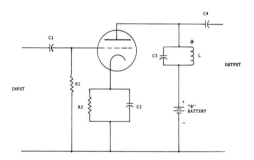

Fig. 87. Amplifier with resonant load.

Linear Amplifier

The output signal of a Class A triode amplifier is essentially a magnified reproduction of its input signal. For example, a 1-volt positive signal will cause a 10-volt drop in plate voltage (because of increase in plate current), and a 1-volt negative signal will cause a 10-volt rise in plate voltage (because of decrease in plate current) when the tube gain is 20 db (ten

81

times voltage amplification). Linear amplification is achieved by appropriate biasing of the grid.

Nonlinear Amplifier

By biasing the grid for nonlinear operation, the input signal is not faithfully reproduced at the output. When cathode bias is used and the value of the cathode resistor is large (10,000 to 50,000 ohms), the bias (grid-to-cathode voltage) will be relatively high. When no signal is present, plate current will be very low. For example, if no-signal plate current is one half milliampere (0.0005 amp) and the cathode resistor has a value of 33,000 ohms, the bias will be 16.5 volts. Now, if the input signal alternatively swings one volt positive and one volt negative, the negative swing will cause only a slight reduction in plate current (small increase in plate voltage), but the positive swing will cause a much greater increase in plate current (large reduction in plate voltage). Hence, the tube is a nonlinear amplifier.

Plate Detector

This nonlinear characteristic makes the circuit useful as a plate detector. When used to receive an AM (amplitude modulated) signal, it will demodulate the signal. But first, the characteristics of an AM signal should be discussed.

When a carrier signal, such as that of a radio, is amplitude modulated by an audio signal (voice, music, or tone), its amplitude is varied. The carrier signal, being high frequency AC, is a sine wave which swings alternately positive and negative at a rate determined by its frequency, as shown in Fig. 88(A).

When it is amplitude modulated, the extent to which the carrier signal swings positive and negative is determined by the amplitude of the modulating signal, as shown in Fig. 88(C). Note that the modulating signal is superimposed on both the positive and negative halves of the carrier signal.

A linear amplifier passes this signal without altering its shape. But if it is fed to a plate detector (Fig. 89), the posi-

82

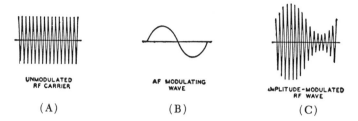

UNMODULATED
RF CARRIER

AF MODULATING
WAVE

AMPLITUDE-MODULATED
RF WAVE

(A)   (B)   (C)

Fig. 88. AM radio signal wave forms (Courtesy of Radio Corporation of America).

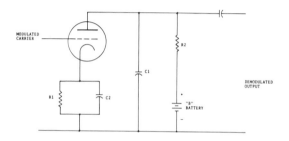

Fig. 89. Simplified circuit of plate dectector.

tive half of the carrier signal is amplified much more than the negative half. The amplitude variations of the positive half of the signal representing modulation remain. Capacitor C^1 (Fig. 89) is a filter which bypasses (shorts out) the carrier signal, leaving only the desired modulation signal. Capacitor C2 shunts R1 for both signals.

Grid Leak Detector

Another type of triode detector circuit, known as a grid leak detector, is shown in Fig. 90. Here, the negative carrier signal excursions cause a large decrease in plate current (rise in plate voltage), and the positive signal excursions cause only a small increase in plate current (drop in plate voltage).

When no carrier signal is present, it would appear that the grid has zero bias. Actually, there is a small negative voltage

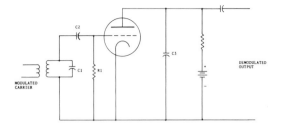

Fig. 90. Grid leak detector.

on the grid, if R1 has a very high value, because of what is known as space charge effect.

When the incoming carrier signal swings positive, the grid is positive with respect to the cathode. This makes the grid function as a plate. Grid current thus flows, causing capacitor C2 to charge in the polarity indicated in the diagram. When the carrier input signal starts swinging negative (becomes less positive), the charge in C2 biases the grid negative with respect to the cathode.

When the carrier signal falls to zero and starts to swing negative, the charge in C2 is in series aiding with the signal voltage, causing the plate current to drop sharply (plate voltage rises). The charge in C2 leaks off slowly through R1 (grid leak), but is replenished during the positive carrier signal excursions.

Positive carrier signal excursions have only a small effect on plate current, but negative carrier signal excursions have a large effect. The modulating signal is thus extracted essentially by the shearing off of one half of the signal envelope, but with polarity opposite to that of a plate detector. Capacitor C3, as before, bypasses the carrier component and leaves the desired signal.

Infinite Impedance Detector

An infinite impedance detector is similar to a plate detector, except that the load is in the cathode circuit, as shown in Fig. 91. Capacitor C2 bypasses the carrier signal, but has little effect on the modulation signal.

84

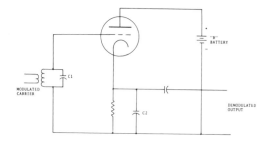

Fig. 91. Infinite impedance detector.

Oscillator

Some 50 years ago, Dr. Lee De Forest, while he was employed by Federal Electric Company (now part of ITT) at Palo Alto, California, and working with the late Cyril F. Elwell and other radio pioneers, discovered feedback while developing an audio amplifier around his Audion triode tube. When the input transformer was placed near the output transformer, a "singing" effect was produced. This phenomenon turned out to be regeneration (positive feedback).

During the same era, Major Edwin H. Armstrong also developed a regenerative circuit, and he and De Forest battled for years over "who did what first." Both men made extraordinary contributions to electronics. Armstrong later invented the superheterodyne and superregenerative circuits as well as FM, all based on De Forest's Audion tube. De Forest's Audion gave birth to the electronics industry. But it was his (or Armstrong's) discovery of regeneration that made radio transmission practical.

With consideration again of the grid leak detector, it can be modified as shown in Fig. 92. Here, we have added another coil, L3, which is known as a tickler or feedback coil. It feeds the signal at the plate back to the grid. If this feedback signal is in phase with the grid, the input signal, already amplified by the tube, will be re-amplified.

When the original signal applies a positive voltage to the grid, plate current rises, causing an increase in the strength

85

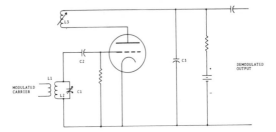

Fig. 92. Regenerative detector.

of the magnetic field around L3. This field induces a voltage in L1 which is amplified by the tube, and still further strengthens the magnetic field around L3.

The circuit will burst into oscillation and function as a generator of AC signals unless the amount of regeneration (positive feedback) is controlled. In early radio receivers, the coupling between L3 and L1 was made variable by making the tickler, L3, rotatable. Regeneration can also be controlled by making C3 a variable capacitor or by varying the plate voltage of the tube.

Colpitts Circuit

Figure 93 shows the circuit of the very popular Colpitts oscillator, which employs a single coil and a pair of capacitors for tuning and feedback control.

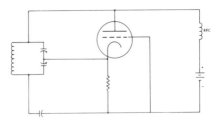

Fig. 93. Colpitts oscillator.

Hartley Circuit

Perhaps the most widely used oscillator circuit is the Hartley, which has several variations. Figure 94 shows a circuit that is commonly used as a tunable oscillator. Tuning is controlled by C1, and regeneration by the location of the tap on L1.

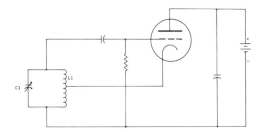

Fig. 94. Hartley oscillator.

Frequency Determination

In an oscillator circuit, frequency is determined by a resonant circuit (L1 and C1 in the above example), which acts like a bell and "rings" at its resonant frequency when struck by an electrical signal. As will be seen later, quartz crystals can be used as the resonant element.

Modulation

An AM signal can be produced by modulation of the amplitude of the signal produced by an oscillator. In the Heising modulator, of which a simple version is shown in Fig. 95, V1 is the oscillator, employing a modified Hartley circuit, and V2 is the modulator. Plate voltage is applied to both tubes through L3, an AF choke (reactor). This choke passes steady DC very readily, but presents a high impedance (reactance) to AF, and resists changes in current flow through it. The RF choke (L2) simply isolates the oscillator from the modulator as far as RF is concerned and has nothing to do with the modulation process.

87

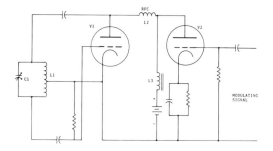

Fig. 95. Amplitude-modulated oscillator.

When the modulating signal causes V2 plate current to rise, V1 plate current drops, and vice versa. It can be put another way: if it is assumed that L1 is the output load for the modulator (V2), it can be seen that the modulating signal will be developed across L1 because of its high inductive reactance. At one instant, this voltage is in series opposing with the DC plate voltage, reducing the plate voltage reaching V1 and, at the same time, reducing its output power. At another instant, the voltage across L1 is in series aiding with the DC plate voltage, and the output power rises. Hence, amplitude modulation is produced by connection of the DC plate voltage and the modulating voltage in series to provide a net plate voltage which varies with the modulating signal.

• PENTODES

The gain of De Forest's Audion (triode) tube was dramatically increased by addition of a second grid (G2) between the first grid (G1) and the plate, and by application of a positive DC voltage to the second grid, known as the screen grid. It accelerates the flow of electrons from the cathode to the plate, whereas the control grid (G1) controls or retards electron flow.

The four-element tube is known as a tetrode. When it was first introduced, it was called a screen grid tube. Later, a fifth

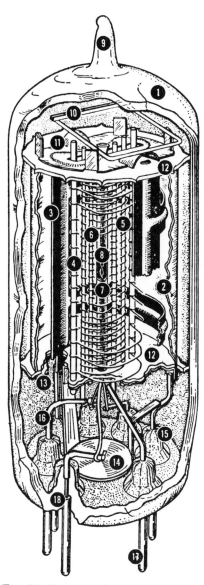

1 — Glass Envelope

2 — Internal Shield

3 — Plate

4 — Grid No. 3 (Suppressor)

5 — Grid No 2 (Screen)

6 — Grid No. 1 (Control Grid)

7 — Cathode

8 — Heater

9 — Exhaust Tip

10 — Getter

11 — Spacer Shield Header

12 — Insulating Spacer

13 — Spacer Shield

14 — Inter-Pin Shield

15 — Glass Button-Stem Seal

16 — Lead Wire

17 — Base Pin

18 — Glass-to-Metal Seal

Fig. 96. Structure of miniature pentode tube (Courtesy of Radio Corporation of America).

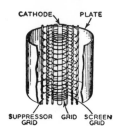

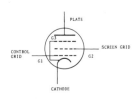

Fig. 97. Relationship of electrodes of a pentode tube (Courtesy of Radio Corporation of America).

Fig. 98. Schematic symbol for pentode tube with suppressor grid connected internally to the cathode.

element, a third grid, was added to form a pentode (Fig. 96). This grid, known as the suppressor grid (G3) (Fig. 97), is placed between the screen grid (G2) and the plate. It is usually connected to the cathode, as shown in Fig. 98. The connection of G3 to the cathode may be external or within the tube, depending on the type of the tube. The function of G3 is to suppress secondary emission of electrons from the plate to the screen.

Resistance-coupled Amplifier

The circuit shown in Fig. 99 is that of a resistance-coupled amplifier stage. It is similar to a triode stage except for the addition of the screen grid (G2) and the suppressor grid (G3) and battery B2, which provides positive screen voltage. Here,

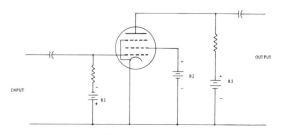

Fig. 99. Pentode amplifier with fixed bias.

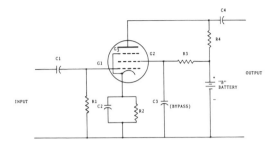

Fig. 100. Resistance-coupled pentode amplifier
with cathode bias.

battery B1 provides negative fixed bias to the control grid,
B2 provides screen voltage, and B3 is the plate voltage source.
A more practical circuit is shown in Fig. 100. Here, cathode
bias is provided by R2, and the positive screen voltage is
obtained from the plate voltage source through R3. Since G2
is positive with respect to the cathode, the screen grid draws
current, and there is a voltage-drop across R2.

Input/Output Isolation

The screen grid performs another function besides that of
accelerating electron flow. It isolates the control grid (G1)
and the plate. With capacitor C2 in the circuit, G2 is at ground
potential at the signal frequency (but not at DC). This isolation is utilized in amplifiers to prevent self-oscillation, which
could otherwise occur when the signal at the plate gets back
to the control grid through the interelectrode capacitance of
the tube.

Fixed-Tuned Amplifier

The circuit of a fixed-tuned amplifier is shown in Fig. 101.
It is similar to an IF (intermediate frequency) stage in a
radio receiver. Transformers T1 and T2 are tuned to the same
frequency. In this circuit, the coils are shown as being adjustable by positioning of their ferrite cores. The coils could be
fixed and their associated capacitors could be variable. If a

91

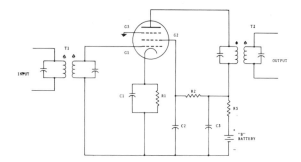

Fig. 101. Tuned pentode amplifier.

triode tube was used, the amplifier would probably oscillate and thus become useless. But, here, the pentode screen grid (G2) is bypassed to ground by C2. This capacitor does not shunt the DC on G2, but does act as a short circuit at the signal frequency. Resistor R3 and capacitor C3 are often used to provide isolation from the plate voltage source, and form what is known as a decoupling network.

Gain Control

The gain of a pentode can be changed by variation of its control grid (G1) bias, its screen grid (G2) voltage, or its suppressor grid (G3) potential, as illustrated previously in Fig. 30 (Chapter 2). In practice, only one of these techniques usually is employed. Control grid bias can be varied or screen voltage can be varied. The gain is reduced by lowering of the screen voltage and vice versa. The suppressor voltage has only a small effect on gain and plate current.

Triode-connected Pentode

Pentode tubes are sometimes used as triodes by connection of the screen and suppressor grids to the plate as shown in Fig. 102. Although pentodes provide much more gain than triodes, the latter are still used. In many circuits, the high gain of a pentode is not required; and in some circuits, a pen-

92

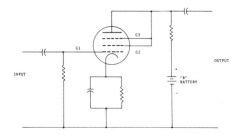

Fig. 102. Triode-connected pentode.

tode is more difficult to use because it requires a higher load impedance than a triode.

Power Pentode

There are two basic types of pentodes, low power and high power. The low-power types are used as voltage amplifiers, as oscillators, and in some control circuits. The high-power types are used in output circuits to drive loads such as loudspeakers and small motors, or in intermediate stages to drive a higher powered amplifier. Another variation of the pentode is the beam power tube (6AQ5, for example). It has a beam deflecting element instead of a suppressor grid. This element is connected within the tube to the cathode.

Power Amplifier

The circuit shown in Fig. 103 is that of a typical power

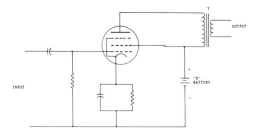

Fig. 103. Power amplifier using beam tube or power pentode.

amplifier stage. The output signal is developed across the primary of the output transformer T, which steps down the voltage and the impedance so that maximum power will be fed to a low impedance load.

If the impedance of the primary of T is 10,000 ohms and the signal across it is at a power level of 1 watt, then the AC voltage across the primary is 100 volts, since the voltage is equal to the square root of watts times impedance. If the load impedance is 4 ohms, and the impedance ratio of T is 10,000:4 (2,500:1), then the AC voltage fed to the load is 2 volts. (The square root of 1 watt times 4 ohms is 2.) We now have a voltage ratio of 100:2 (50:1) and an impedance ratio of 10,000:4 (2,500:1). The transformer turns ratio and the voltage ratio are the same, but the impedance ratio is equal to their square.

If the output transformer were not used and the low impedance load were connected directly into the plate circuit of the tube, then the AC voltage drop across the load (if its impedance is 4 ohms) would be only about 40 millivolts (0.04 volt). The power consumed by the load would be less than a milliwatt.

Therefore, a transformer is used to match the power source (tube) to the load. Although the voltage is stepped down, the power is not, except for the small losses in the transformer.

Frequency Multiplier

Pentodes are often used as frequency multipliers. In Fig. 104, a signal is fed into the control grid through C2. The plate tank circuit (L1, C1) is tuned to a harmonic (multiple) of the input signal frequency. For example, if the input signal is at 1.5 MHz, the circuit functions as a frequency doubler, or if the input is at 1 MHz and the output is at 3 MHz, it is a frequency tripler.

The tube is operated as a Class C amplifier. Plate current flows only during a portion of the time the grid is driven positive by the input signal. Because of this fact, the output signal is distorted and rich in harmonics. With tuning of the out-

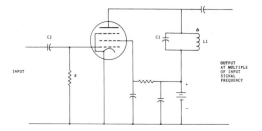

Fig. 104. Frequency multiplier.

put circuit to one of the harmonics, the input signal frequency and unwanted harmonics are suppressed, and a clean signal at the desired harmonic frequency results because of the flywheel effect of the tuned circuit.

Note that in Fig. 104, the control grid is connected directly to common ground through a resistor. When there is no input signal, control grid bias will be zero, and excessive plate current will flow. But when a strong input signal is present, the control grid and cathode function as a shunt diode. Capacitor C2 charges up and stores a negative DC voltage, which provides sufficient bias for Class C operation. The grid is biased so far negative that plate current flows only during a portion of the positive excursions of the input voltage.

Oscillator

Pentodes are also used as oscillators in a variety of circuits. One of the most popular is the electron-coupled oscillator

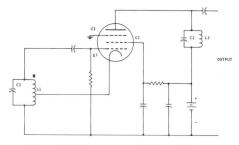

Fig. 105. Electron-coupled oscillator.

shown in Fig. 105. Here, the control grid is used in a Hartley circuit with the screen grid (G2) functioning as the oscillator plate. The plate current variations caused by oscillation produce an output signal across C2–L2 that may be tuned to one of the oscillator's harmonics. The oscillator and output circuits are electronically coupled, but otherwise isolated from each other.

• HEPTODES

Many radio receivers and some industrial electronic devices employ a pentagrid converter tube (6BE6, for example) as a frequency converter. The tube functions as both a mixed and a local oscillator. As shown in Fig. 106, the tube has five grids. The suppressor grid (nearest the plate) is connected internally to the cathode. Grids 2 and 4 are connected together and to a positive DC voltage. Grid 4 acts as a screen grid. The incoming signal is applied to grid 3 (between grids 2 and 4). Grid 2 functions as the plate of the local oscillator, and grid 1 as its control grid. Thus, both the local oscillator signal and the incoming signal modulate the electron stream. The output circuit is tuned to the sum or difference of the two frequencies.

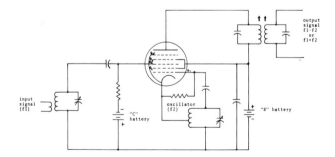

Fig. 106. Frequency converter employing pentagrid converter tube.

Oscillator/Modulator

The pentagrid tube can also be used in other applications, such as the oscillator, modulator, and carrier amplifier of an AM transmitter. The oscillator circuit may be the same as in the previous circuit, but the plate circuit is tuned to the same frequency as the oscillator or to one of its harmonics. The modulating signal is fed to grid 3 to vary plate current. As in a frequency converter, the two signals are heterodyned, causing the output signal to consist of the carrier plus the sum and difference beats, producing upper and lower sidebands. If the carrier is at 1000 KHz, for example, and the modulating signal is at 3 KHz (3000 Hz), there will be output signals at 1003 KHz, 1000 KHz and 997 KHz (upper sideband, carrier, and lower sideband).

• INDICATOR TUBES

Electron eye indicator tubes (Fig. 107) are used as tuning indicators in radio receivers and in various kinds of electronic equipment. At the end of the tube is a round phosphorescent screen that has a green glow. The entire screen is green (eye open) or only partially green, the unilluminated

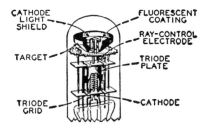

Fig. 107. Construction of electron eye tube (Courtesy of Radio Corporation of America).

area being known as the shadow, as shown in Fig. 108. When the shadow angle is about 100 degrees, the eye is said to be closed.

The value of the grid voltage determines the shadow angle of an electron eye tube of the 6E5 or 6U5 type. As shown in Fig. 109, the tube consists of two triodes. The plate of the triode at the left is connected internally to the grid of the other triode, forming a direct-coupled amplifier. The plate of the other triode is known as the target, to which the plate supply voltage is applied directly.

In the diagram, a negative DC voltage is applied to the control grid from potentiometer R1. This reduces the plate current flowing through R2, causing the grid of the second triode to become more positive and the shadow angle to be reduced. When a 6E5 tube is used, the shadow angle is zero

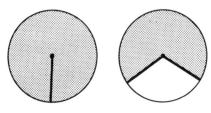

FULL NEGATIVE
VOLTAGE ON GRID

ZERO GRID
VOLTAGE

Fig. 108. Indications of electron eye tube.

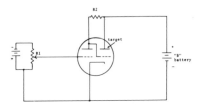

Fig. 109. Demonstration circuit for electron eye tube.

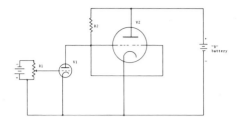

Fig. 110. Circuit for demonstrating dual
electron eye tube.

with 8 volts negative applied to the control grid, and 250 volts
positive applied to the target.

This type of tube can be used as a go no-go indicator or
relative voltage or signal level indicator.

Another type of electron eye (6AF6G, for example) is used
in the circuit shown in Fig. 110. Here, V1 is an external control tube, and V2 is the eye tube. The shadow angle is zero
degrees when the grid potential is 155 volts positive, and
widens as the grid voltage is reduced. When a negative DC
voltage is applied to the grid of V1, its plate current is reduced,
as is the voltage-drop across R2, causing V2 grid voltage to
rise (shadow angle decreases). When V1 grid voltage is decreased (less negative), the shadow angle is widened, since
V2 grid voltage is reduced because V1 plate current is increased.

This type of electron eye tube has two control grids and
two shadows. In the diagram, both grids are connected together and both shadow angles are controlled simultaneously.
However, they can be used independently. Two circuits can
be monitored simultaneously.

• TRIPLE OUTPUT TUBES

The schematic symbol of still another type of tube
is shown in Fig. 111. Here, there is one grid controlling electron flow from the cathode to three independent plates (plate

99

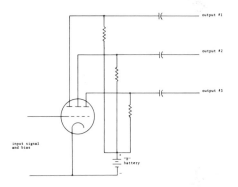

Fig. 111. Simplified diagram for triple-plate tube.

load circuits not shown). This kind of tube can be used to distribute one signal to three different circuits that are isolated from each other.

• GATED BEAM TUBES

One of the most interesting tubes is the gated beam tube (3BN6, 6BN6, for example); its schematic symbol is the same as for a pentode, since it has three grids. How-

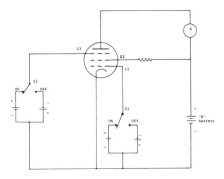

Fig. 112. Demonstration circuit for gated beam tube.

100

ever, the tube is quite different from a pentode. In a pentode, the suppressor grid has only a small effect on plate current. The quadrature grid (G3) of the gated beam tube, on the other hand, has a great effect on plate current. In Fig. 112, switch S1 is used to apply either a negative or positive DC voltage to the control grid (G1), and S2 to the quadrature grid (G3). If both S1 and S2 are set at the "on" position (positive), the tube will conduct, drawing maximum plate current as indicated by milliammeter A. When either S1 or S2 is set at the "off" position (negative), the tube will stop conducting, and plate current will drop to zero.

Amplitude Limiter

This type of tube makes an excellent amplitude limiter. A typical limiter circuit is shown in Fig. 113. Whenever the input signal swings negative, plate current is reduced, and cut off when the signal is about two volts negative. On positive swings, plate current rises and reaches maximum (saturation) when the signal is about two volts positive. Hence, the output signal cannot rise above a specific level. The limiting action is very fast, since no capacitor-resistor combination is employed in the grid circuit. Other limiters with such a combination are slower.

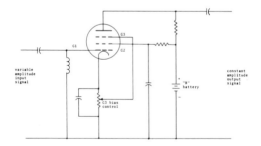

Fig. 113. Gated beam amplitude limiter.

Phase Detector

The gated beam tube is widely used in TV sets and FM communications receivers as a combined limiter and FM detector, using a circuit like the one shown in Fig. 114.

Here, the quadrature grid is connected to a resonant circuit (L-C), which is tuned to the same frequency as the incoming signal. When the incoming FM signal frequency changes (modulation), the quadrature grid resonant circuit tends to remain excited at its resonant frequency. The phase relationships of the signals at the control and quadrature grid change, causing the plate current to consist of a train of pulses, the width of which depends on grid gating. The average plate current, therefore, represents the audio signal.

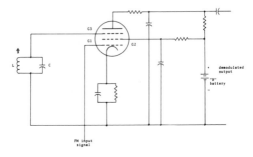

Fig. 114. Gated beam tube phase detector and limiter.

6 ⋮ Transistors

A transistor (Fig. 115) is like a tube in many respects. In some applications it is better; in others it is not as good or cannot be used as yet.

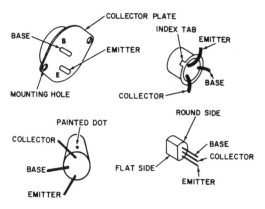

Fig. 115. Various types of transistors showing connecting leads.

As was stated in the previous chapter, the grid of a tube is like a brake. It retards the flow of electrons. In a transistor, the base is the control element, and it acts as an accelerator.

Electronic Switch

While transistors are replacing tubes in many applications and often perform the same basic functions, they differ operationally. Figure 116 shows the schematic symbols of both a tube and a transistor. The emitter (E) of a transistor is the equivalent of the cathode (K) of a tube, the collector (C) is the equivalent of the plate (P), and the base (B) is the equivalent of the grid (G). It is the signal applied to the grid of a tube that controls plate current. The signal applied to the base of a transistor controls its collector current.

 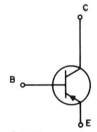

Fig. 116. Triode tube and PNP transistor.

But there is a difference. The grid of a tube is ordinarily reverse-biased to limit plate current to a safe level. If the reverse bias (negative voltage) is increased, plate current decreases. If the reverse bias is lowered, plate current rises.

A transistor, on the other hand, is usually forward-biased by application of a DC voltage to its base. Otherwise, collector current does not flow. When it is forward-biased, increasing the forward bias causes collector current to rise. Decreasing the forward bias causes collector current to be lowered. Hence, the effect of a signal is just the opposite of that in a tube.

In an electronic switch application, a positive-going voltage is applied to the grid of a tube to raise plate current high enough to energize a relay or other output device. In the case of a PNP transistor, a negative voltage is applied to increase collector current through the load.

104

AC Amplifier

In a practical amplifier circuit, fixed forward bias usually is applied to the base of a transistor. This bias causes collector current to flow. Its magnitude is raised and lowered by the signal. In Fig. 117, forward bias is obtained from a voltage divider (R1–R2) across the supply voltage (battery). The AC signal path is shown in heavy lines. The circuit, although the same as in Fig. 117, is usually drawn as in Fig. 118.

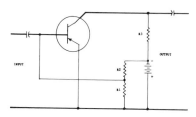

Fig. 117. AC amplifier with fixed bias.

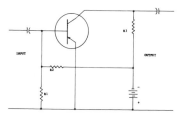

Fig. 118. Usual way to illustrate Fig. 117.

Heat Problems

Heat is generated in the transistor at what is known as the junction. In Fig. 116, when S is open, very little heat is generated because the collector current is low. When S is closed, heat is generated. However, if the forward bias is great enough to saturate the transistor, less heat is generated, because the resistivity of the transistor is lower (conductivity is higher).

105

When a transistor is required to handle high current, a heat sink is used to dissipate the heat. Whether a heat sink is used or not, thermal runaway can occur in some circuits unless precautions are taken. When the junction temperature rises, current flow also rises, causing the junction temperature to increase further. In the circuit in Fig. 119, thermal runaway is prevented by addition of R4 in series with the emitter and by connection of R2 to the collector, instead of directly to the supply voltage. Capacitor C3 across R4 reduces degeneration in the same manner as in a tube cathode circuit.

When the collector current rises, the emitter current also rises, causing an increase in the voltage-drop across R4. This voltage opposes the forward bias on the base, reducing it and the collector current. Also, when the collector voltage drops because of an increase in collector current, the forward bias fed to the base through R2 is reduced, causing collector current to decrease.

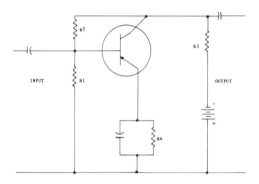

Fig. 119. Amplifier with thermal run-away protection.

NPN Transistor

All of the circuits shown so far employ a PNP transistor. An NPN transistor is used in the circuit in Fig. 120. It is the same as the circuit of Figs. 117 and 118, except that the supply

106

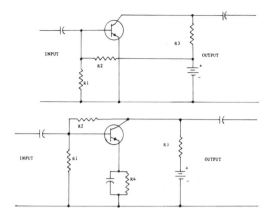

Fig. 120. NPN transistor circuits.

voltage polarity is reversed. Note that in the symbol of a PNP transistor, the emitter arrow points toward the base, and in an NPN transistor it points away from the base. To forward bias an NPN transistor, the base is made positive with respect to the emitter, a procedure just the opposite of that for a PNP transistor.

Emitter-follower

An emitter-follower or common collector amplifier circuit is shown in Fig. 121. This is similar to a tube cathode-follower circuit. The output signal is developed across R3 in the emitter circuit instead of in the collector circuit.

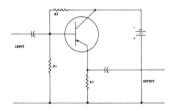

Fig. 121. Emitter-follower circuit.

Common Base Amplifier

A common base amplifier circuit is shown in Fig. 122. It is similar to a grounded grid tube circuit. The signal is fed into the emitter and taken out from the collector. The base is forward biased by battery B2, which makes the emitter positive with respect to the base (base negative with respect to the emitter).

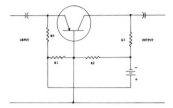

Fig. 122. Common base amplifier.

DC Amplifier

Transistors are often used as switches or DC amplifiers to control devices. In Fig. 123, relay K is controlled through transistor Q by opening and closing of switch S. When S is open, very little collector current flows, and the relay is de-energized. When S is closed, collector current flows, and the

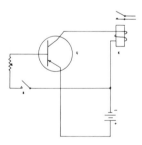

Fig. 123. DC amplifier for controlling relay.

relay is pulled in. Although the switch could be used to control the relay directly, the transistor makes it possible to use a very light duty switch.

With the use of a potentiometer (R1) to vary the forward-bias voltage, as in Fig. 124, an analog DC amplifier is formed. The brilliance of lamp I can be controlled by adjustment of R1. A small change in forward bias (base current) causes a large change in collector current.

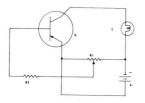

Fig. 124. Analog DC amplifier.

Logic Circuits

Transistors are widely used in computer and control circuits. For example, a pair of transistors can be used to form an OR gate, as shown in Fig. 125. When both S1 and S2 are open, the relay (K) is de-energized. When either S1 or S2 is closed, the relay is pulled in.

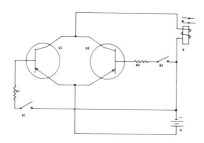

Fig. 125. OR gate.

• ANALOG APPLICATIONS

Detector

Let us compare transistors with tubes in nonlinear applications. In Fig. 89 (Chapter 5), a triode tube is used as a plate detector. The grid is biased negative (reverse biased) by cathode R1. When no signal is present, plate current is very small. A signal causes plate current to rise sharply whenever the signal drives the grid positive (forward bias). When the signal swings negative, reverse bias is further increased. Since the tube is normally biased to keep plate current low, it cannot drop much (only to zero) during negative input signal excursions. Hence, the negative half of the AM signal envelope is essentially sheared off, and the audio signal on the positive half is present at the output.

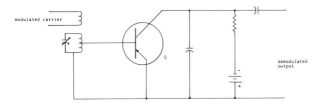

Fig. 126. Transistor AM detector.

The transistor Q in Fig. 126 normally has no base bias. Forward bias is required to cause collector current to flow. When a signal is received, the transistor base is forward biased during the negative signal excursions, causing the collector current to flow. During positive signal excursions, the base is reverse biased and no collector current flows. Hence, detector action is achieved.

The two circuits (Figs. 89 and 126) are similar. If the transistor is an NPN type instead of the PNP type shown, collector current would flow during positive input signal excursions, as in the case of the tube.

Note the difference in the coil connections in Fig. 89. All of L2 (a parallel resonant circuit) is used to drive the grid.

110

But in Fig. 126, the base connection is made at a tap on the coil. The tube grid does not draw current, and its extremely high input resistance does not load down the resonant circuit; but the transistor base draws current. If it were applied across the whole coil, selectivity would be reduced because of loading of the resonant circuit.

Tuned Amplifier

A pentode tube is shown in a tuned amplifier circuit in Fig. 101 (Chapter 5). The control grid is reverse biased slightly by the cathode resistor. The signal causes plate current alternately to rise and fall, approximately at equal amounts.

Since both the input and output resistances are high, parallel-resonant circuits can be used at both ends without tapping down to reduce impedance and loading, as is required when a transistor is used (Fig. 127). Here, the previous transistor stage, or low impedance input, is fed to a tap on L1. The parallel-resonant circuit (L1–C1) is inductively coupled to L2, which feeds the transistor base at low impedance. The collector of the transistor is fed to a tap on L3, and inductive coupling is used to feed the next stage.

The tube in Fig. 101 is reverse biased, whereas the transistor in Fig. 127 is forward biased by the voltage divider. Capacitor C2 grounds the bottom of L2 at the signal frequency, but not for DC.

Note the supply voltages in all of these diagrams. The transistors require low voltages in the 1.5 to 12 volt range,

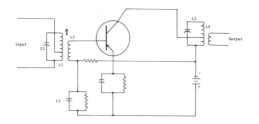

Fig. 127. Tuned transistor amplifier.

whereas the tubes require a minimum of about 45 volts, and even as much as 300 volts.

AF Amplifier

An audio amplifier circuit is shown in Fig. 128. In a tube circuit, the grid is reverse biased to allow only a certain amount of plate current to flow at all times. The input resistance is high, since the grid draws no current.

The input resistance of the transistor in Fig. 128 is much lower, since the input signal must deliver base current when it swings negative. The value of C1 may be several microfarads.

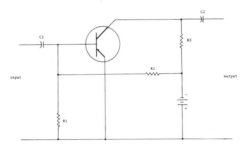

Fig. 128. Transistor AF amplifier.

The base is forward biased so that some collector current flows at all times. The input signal causes collector current to increase when it is negative, and to decrease when it is positive. With the use of an NPN transistor (PNP shown), the opposite would be true.

Oscillator

An oscillator circuit is shown in Fig. 129. In the circuit shown in Fig. 92 (Chapter 5), the signal is fed back in phase from the plate of the triode tube to the grid by inductive coupling of the tickler coil to the grid coil. Reverse grid bias is developed by the grid capacitor and the grid leak.

112

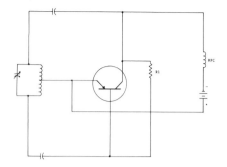

Fig. 129. Hartley oscillator employing a
PNP transistor.

Regenerative feedback is also provided in the circuit shown
in Fig. 129, in which a transistor is used. Here, the transistor
is used in a common emitter configuration. The base is forward
biased by R1.

Frequency Converter

In Chapter 5, the use of a pentagrid converter tube (heptode) as a frequency converter was discussed. The oscillator
employs the cathode, the first grid, and the second grid (functioning as a plate). The input signal is fed to the third grid,
which is isolated from the first and fifth grids by the second

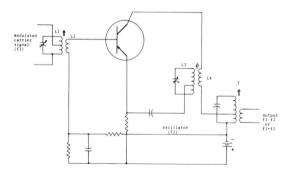

Fig. 130. Autodyne converter.

113

and fourth grids (functioning as screen grid). The input signal at the third grid and the oscillator signal at the first grid both modulate the cathode-to-plate electron stream.

A single transistor can be used as an autodyne frequency converter in a circuit similar to that shown in Fig. 130. The transistor functions both as a nonlinear amplifier (detector) and as the local oscillator. The input signal is fed to the transistor base. The tickler coil (L4) is in series with the output load (primary of transformer T). The input signal at 1000 KHz, for example, modulates collector current, as does the oscillator signal at 1455 KHz, producing a 455 KHz beat that is picked off by the transformer.

• SUMMARY

There are thousands of types of transistors, many of them interchangeable even if they have different type numbers. There are two basic families of transistors—small signal transistors and power transistors. There are also tetrode, unijunction, field effect, drift, mesa, and other types of transistors, which, because of space limitations, are not covered in this chapter. The basic transistor circuits discussed above are the ones most commonly used, and the information given here should be adequate for a basic understanding of transistors.

7 ⋮ Electronic Switch And Control Elements

One of the most useful applications of tubes and semiconductors is as a switch. The amplification characteristics permit control of a high power load with much lower power. A vacuum tube or a transistor functions as a non-latching switch. An input signal is required for maintaining load current. A thyratron (gas tube) or a silicon-controlled rectifier (SCR), on the other hand, can be used as a latching switch. Once triggered by an input signal, the device allows load current to flow continuously.

• DC CIRCUITS

Vacuum Tube Switch

Figure 131 presents a vacuum tube triode (filament circuit not shown) with lamp I as the load. When switch S is open, the grid is biased negative by battery B2 through resistor R2. Plate current does not flow, and the lamp does not light. The negative grid bias acts as a brake, retarding flow of electrons from the tube cathode to its plate.

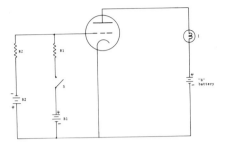

Fig. 131. Electronic switch for control
of small lamp.

When S is closed, a positive voltage from B1 is applied
through R1 to the grid, reducing the negative bias on the grid
and allowing plate current to flow through the lamp. The
lamp glows only when S is closed.

Thyratron Switch

But if we substitute a thyratron for the vacuum tube, as
shown in Fig. 132, the lamp will become lighted when S is
closed and will remain lighted after S is reopened. This is
true because a thyratron will continue to conduct once it has
been fired by a positive input signal.

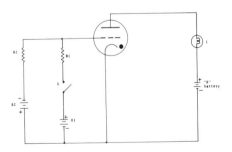

Fig. 132. Thyratron switch for lamp control.

Transistor Switch

In the transistor circuit shown in Fig. 133, when S is open, there is no forward bias on the transistor base, and no collector current flows through lamp I. When S is closed, negative forward bias is applied through R1 to the transistor base. This bias causes the transistor to conduct, and collector current flows through the lamp. As soon as S is reopened, collector current ceases, and the lamp is extinguished.

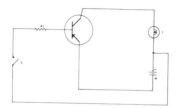

Fig. 133. Transistor switch for
lamp control.

SCR Switch

But if we substitute an SCR for the transistor, as shown in Fig. 134, we have a latching-type switch. When a trigger voltage is applied to the gate of the SCR through R1 by the closing of S, the SCR (like a thyratron) is triggered into conduction, causing the lamp to light. When S is reopened, the SCR continues to conduct, and the lamp remains lighted.

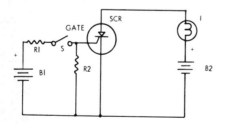

Fig. 134. SCR latching switch circuit.

The lamp can be extinguished by disconnection of the supply voltage (B2) or by added circuitry, as shown in Fig. 135. Here, closing S1 momentarily triggers the SCR into conduction. The lamp lights, and capacitor C charges through resistor R3. With closing of S2 momentarily, the charge in C is applied to the anode and cathode of SCR. Since the polarity of the charge in C is in opposition to the supply voltage, the anode of SCR is made momentarily negative with respect to its cathode (reverse biased), causing it to stop conducting and the lamp to be extinguished. Reclosure of S1 momentarily again triggers SCR into conduction.

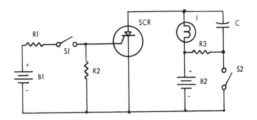

Fig. 135. Latch-unlatch SCR circuit.

• AC CIRCUITS

Switched Tube Rectifier

When a vacuum tube is used to control a load operated from an AC source, as shown in Fig. 136, the lamp is lighted only as long as S is closed. The load current, however, is pulsating DC, since the tube functions as a rectifier.

Thyratron Rectifier

The same is true when a thyratron is used. When the source voltage is DC, as in Fig. 132, the thyratron continues to conduct after it has been fired. But when the source voltage is AC, as in Fig. 137, the thyratron conducts only during the positive AC half-cycles. During the other half-cycles, the

118

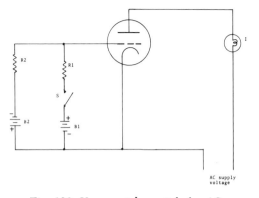

Fig. 136. Vacuum tube switch for AC.

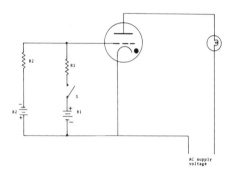

Fig. 137. Thyratron switch for AC.

thyratron plate is negative with respect to its cathode and cannot conduct. It is necessary, therefore, to keep S closed to maintain the lamp lighted, since the thyratron must be re-triggered every cycle.

Silicon-controlled Rectifier

An SCR in an AC circuit operates in a similar manner. In Fig. 138, the circuit is the same as that previously shown in Fig. 135, except that AC is used as the power source instead of DC. The SCR can conduct only during the half-cycles that its anode is positive with respect to its cathode and must be retriggered every cycle.

119

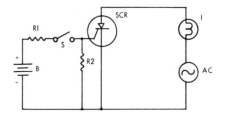

Fig. 138. Non-latching SCR control circuit.

When S is kept closed in the circuit in Fig. 138, the SCR is automatically triggered. Thus, the lamp remains lighted when S is closed, and it is extinguished when S is open.

A lamp has been shown as the load in all of the examples given above, but other loads can be used. The SCR is being used widely in many control applications. It is superior to a thyratron in that it will operate at lower voltages and is available in a variety of ratings. The SCR is used as a rectifier in sophisticated power supplies, where voltage regulation is obtained by triggering of the SCR devices as required to control the conduction time per cycle.

8 : Basic
: Electronic
: Systems

Electronic systems consist of equipment (system components) and, in some cases, include subsystems which are "systems within a system" (see Fig. 139). Examination of various kinds of industrial electronic systems proves that they are not as complex as many persons think they are.

Fig. 139. Photoelectric scanning system. Scanner head (E8S11G) responds to light from retroflector (P380). When flap-lifter detects carton with flaps not securely glued, light beam is broken and ejector removes faulty carton from conveyor belt. (Courtesy of Autotron, Inc.)

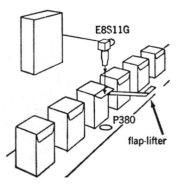

• CONTROL SYSTEMS

The control of machines and devices by electronic means, rather than purely electrical or electromechanical means, has distinct advantages. Response time is much faster, sparking contacts are often eliminated, control circuitry can employ smaller or fewer wires or no wires at all, and overload and other protection is faster and more dependable.

Local Control

A motor is usually controlled by a switch connected between the power line and the motor, or the switch may be a heavy duty relay (magnetic contactor) controlled by push buttons. With electronics, the relays may be replaced with so-called controlled rectifiers (SCR, for example) which have no moving contacts. The control element may be a push button, proximity sensor, or other type of sensor. Almost everyone is familiar with elevator call buttons which need only be touched, not pushed.

Remote Control

With the use of electronics, one or more control points can be provided, directly connected to the controlling devices or with the use of radio in lieu of direct wire connections. For example, cranes are controlled from the plant floor by a per-

Fig. 140. Portable crane control transmitter (Courtesy of Motorola, Inc.).

son who simply operates levers or pushes buttons to control
the movements of the crane (see Fig. 140).

Variable Control

The speed of a motor can be controlled and regulated with
the use of electromechanical techniques or electronics. With
electronics, sparking contacts and wearing parts can be
avoided. Smoother speed control and stabilization of speed
at the selected value are made possible. Here, thyratron tubes
or solid state controlled rectifiers can be used.

Automatic Control

A motor or complex machine can be controlled automatically
with electronic devices. Automatic control systems range in
complexity from a simple sensing system to one employing a
computer.

Open Loop Systems

An open loop system is one in which the controlled device
does not have any effect on its controller. For example, in
Fig. 141, the motor speed is "controlled," but not "regulated."

Fig. 141. Open loop control system.

Closed Loop Systems

In a closed loop system, the controlled device feeds back
information to its controller. For example, in Fig. 142, the
speed of the motor is sensed. When the speed is not correct,
an "error" signal is transmitted to the controller, which automatically corrects the speed.

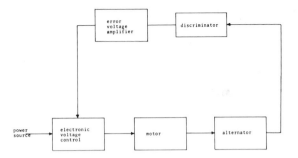

Fig. 142. Closed loop control system.

Servo Systems

A servo system is a closed loop system. In Fig. 143, for example, the position of potentiometer R2 is automatically rotated when potentiometer R1 is turned manually. When their respective output voltages are not the same, an error voltage is fed into the amplifier, which causes the drive motor of R2 to run until no error voltage exists. The motor driving R2 usually drives an indicator or a machine also.

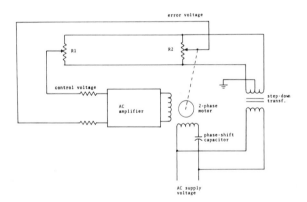

Fig. 143. Simple servo system.

• MONITORING SYSTEMS

Electronic devices can be used to count events or items, and to sense changes in temperature, speed, dimensions of products being manufactured, and so on.

Counters

One of the most widely used industrial electronic devices is the electronic counter (see Fig. 144). It can be used to count packages or other items as they pass by on a conveyor belt. A counter can also be used to tally events and machine operations. The sensing device may be a switch, photoelectric cell, thermistor, or other type of sensor.

Fig. 144. Electronic counter (Courtesy of Veeder-Root, Inc.).

Alarms

Sensors can be used to actuate alarm systems. For example, a thermistor may be used to monitor bearing temperature. When the temperature rises above a predetermined point, an alarm is sounded or the machine is automatically shut down.

• COMMUNICATIONS

Initially, electronics was used only for communications. First it was called wireless, then radio. Now elec-

125

tronics covers all devices and systems employing tubes or transistors or other semiconductor devices.

Radio

In industry, radio is used mainly for two-way communication between personnel on foot, on board vehicles, or at fixed locations (Fig. 145). A two-way radio system may employ base stations (at fixed locations), mobile units (on vehicles), and personal portable transceivers (walkie-talkies).

Radio operating on microwave frequencies is used for interplant communication and data transmission (Fig. 146).

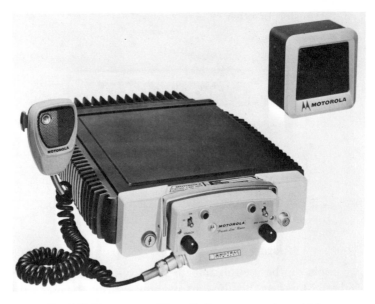

Fig. 145. Two-way mobile radio for use on motor vehicles.

Television

Closed circuit television (CCTV) is widely used in industry for surveillance and observation of phenomena at dangerous locations. A CCTV system can be very simple, consisting of a

126

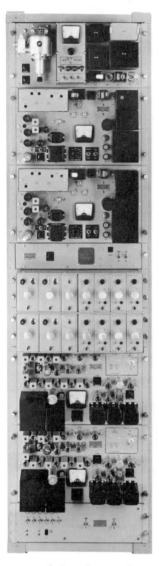

Fig. 146. Microwave terminal for plant-to-plant communications and data transmission (Courtesy of Cardion Communications Corp.).

127

Fig. 147. Closed circuit television camera.

Fig. 148. CCTV monitor.

camera (Fig. 147) and a monitor (Fig. 148), which may be a standard television receiver; or a system may employ several cameras, numerous monitors, and even a video-tape recorder.

Sound Systems

Almost every plant is equipped with a loudspeaker paging system, employing one or more microphones, an amplifier, and a large number of loudspeakers. Some systems are designed so that paging calls can be made from any telephone extension simply by dialing a specified number.

Intercom

Wired intercom systems became available about 30 years ago. A wired intercom system (Fig. 149) is quite similar to a paging system, except that it provides two-way communication on a simplex basis (one direction at a time). An intercom system may consist of one master unit and a number of slave units, each employing loudspeakers alternately as a microphone and as a loudspeaker. Some systems employ master units only, enabling any unit to communicate with another.

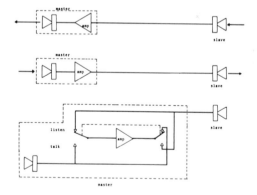

Fig. 149. Wired intercom system. (A) Master in "listen" position. (B) Master in "talk" position. (C) Block diagram of basic wired intercom system.

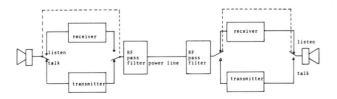

Fig. 150. Basic, single-frequency simplex wireless intercom system.

Although all units of a wired intercom system are interconnected through wires, so-called wireless intercom systems employ the electric power lines as the transmission medium (Fig. 150). Each unit is actually a low power radio transceiver (transmitter-receiver) employing what is known as carrier current transmission.

Telephone

Telephones in a plant are usually furnished and maintained by the local telephone company. Many plants, however, have their own private, intraplant telephone system that is maintained by plant personnel. A telephone system usually consists of a dial or manual switchboard and a large number of telephone extensions connected to the switchboard through wires.

Facsimile

Some plants employ facsimile machines for transmission of graphic information within a plant, with wires to interconnect the machines. One machine scans the document, and it is reproduced at one or more other machines.

Teletypewriters

Printed information can be transmitted from one location to another by teletypewriters interconnected by wires. Often they are connected in "round robin" fashion. When so connected, all machines type whatever information is being trans-

130

mitted. Sometimes, means are provided for transmission of information to one or more selected machines only.

• COMPUTERS

Very rarely are plant personnel required to maintain computers (Fig. 151). Maintenance service is usually provided by the computer manufacturer or an outside service organization. Small computers used for machine control are sometimes maintained by plant personnel.

Fig. 151. The computer has become a vital industrial tool.

• SYSTEMS COMPONENTS

As stated before, an electronic system consists of various pieces of equipment, all of which may be contained within a single enclosure or located at different points. Often, each device (piece of equipment) is called a system component. Sometimes, a unit of equipment is actually a subsystem. An electronic system may appear complex, but it usually consists of a multiplicity of simple system components. Examination of some of the basic components follows.

Amplifiers

There are many kinds of amplifiers. All are basically similar. Most employ two or more amplifier stages in cascade (output of one stage is fed to the input of the next stage for re-amplification). They amplify electrical signals. The gain (amount of amplification) of an amplifier is usually rated in decibels (db). An amplifier with a gain of 6 db increases voltage by 2:1 and power by 4:1, but a typical amplifier usually has much more gain. For example, if an amplifier has a gain of 80 db, it will deliver 100,000,000 times greater power than that fed into it.

For some purposes, DC amplifiers are used (Fig. 152). A DC amplifier is capable of amplifying DC signals (zero frequency). Some have wide bandwidth and are capable of passing AC signals at frequencies up to 100 KHz (100,000 cycles per second), or even higher. Such amplifiers are often used to sense a DC signal from a sensor such as a resistive strain gauge. Strain causes sensor output voltage to change. This is still DC. But vibration may cause the DC voltage to fluctuate at a high frequency; this is now modulated DC, a form of AC.

Audio frequency (AF) amplifiers (Fig. 153) are used in sound systems and in some control systems that employ an AC signal. Typically, an AF amplifier passes frequencies from 50 Hz (50 cycles per second) to 20 KHz (20,000 cycles per second).

Video amplifiers are similar and are used for amplifying television and other high frequency signals, such as short pulses; they usually have a frequency response ranging from DC (or almost) to several megahertz (megacycles per second).

132

Fig. 152. DC amplifier. Used widely in electronic instrumentation and control systems.

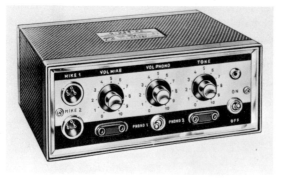

Fig. 153. Audio frequency amplifier.

Radio frequency (RF) amplifiers may be tuned to pass only a narrow band of frequencies, or may be of the broadband type. RF amplifiers are used in radio equipment, in wireless intercoms, and in some signal transmission systems.

Servo amplifiers are used in control systems and may be DC or AF amplifiers, depending on the type of signal used.

Sensors

A sensor senses physical changes and converts them into electrical changes. There are many kinds of sensors, some of which are described below.

A strain gauge (invented by Edward Simmons) consists of a sensing resonator connected in a bridge circuit with other resistors. The resistance of the sensing resistor varies with strain applied to it, causing the bridge to become unbalanced and to change its output voltage.

There are many types of light-sensitive sensors, including photoelectric cells, selenium cells, cadmium sulphide cells, and light-sensitive diodes and transistors. The conductivity of a photoelectric cell or a cadmium sulphide or light-sensitive semiconductor device (diode or transistor) increases with the intensity of the light it detects. A selenium or solar cell, on the other hand, generates an electrical voltage proportional to the amount of light it detects.

A thermistor changes its resistance as the heat it senses changes. The higher the temperature it senses, the greater its conductivity (resistance lowers).

An accelerometer senses changes in acceleration and usually delivers a DC output signal. A microphone senses changes in sound waves and air pressure and delivers an AC output signal.

Logic

Digital systems often employ logic circuits, such as AND, OR, NOR, and NOT gates, which deliver an output signal or provide an electrical path when input signal requirements are satisfied.

134

Switches

There are many types of electronic switches that deliver a voltage or provide an electrical path when actuated by an electrical signal.

An SCR (silicon-controlled rectifier), for example (see Fig. 134, Chapter 7), keeps a circuit open until a triggering signal is applied to its gate. When used in a DC circuit, an SCR provides an electrical path through itself continuously after it is triggered. It will open only when the DC potential across its anode and cathode is removed. In an AC circuit, an SCR stops conducting as soon as its trigger voltage is removed. A thyratron tube operates in the same manner.

A flip-flop (bistable multivibrator) acts as a so-called three-way light switch (Fig. 154). When triggered, it provides a DC output signal at one of its two output terminals, but none at the other. When it is triggered again, a DC output signal is available at the opposite output terminal.

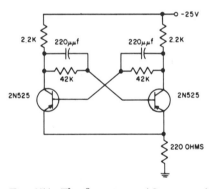

Fig. 154. Flip-flop circuit (Courtesy of General Electric Co.).

Diodes are also used as switches. To provide an open circuit, the diode is reverse biased (anode is negative with respect to cathode) by a fixed bias voltage. When triggered by a voltage that offsets the reverse bias, the diode provides an electrical conducting path.

Transistors and tubes are also used as electronic switches. When the base of a transistor is reverse biased (or has no forward bias), no collector current flows. When the base is forward biased, collector current flows through the load. In the case of a tube, plate current flows through the load only when the reverse bias (negative voltage) is removed from the grid, or reduced sufficiently to allow plate current to flow.

Matrix

A matrix employing diodes is used to channel current flow (Fig. 155). It is like a crossbar switch. When a signal voltage is applied to two of its legs, the diode connected to the legs conducts, and an output signal is delivered to the selected circuit.

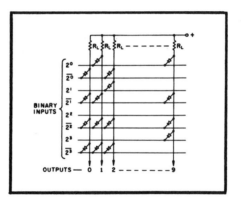

Fig. 155. Simple matrix used as a decoder (Courtesy of Burroughs Corp.).

Oscillators

An electronic oscillator is an AC generator. The frequency of the AC depends on the electrical values of the frequency-determining elements, which may be combinations of inductance and capacitance (LC) or resistance and capacitance

136

(RC). Or the frequency-determining element may be a quartz crystal, vibrating reed resonator, tuning fork, or Twintron (Fig. 156). The Twintron is similar to, but more stable than a tuning fork.

Fig. 156. Twintron electromechanical resonator.

An oscillator depends on amplification and feedback. An oscillator is actually an amplifier the output of which is fed back to the input in phase. Thus, the output signal is re-amplified, and oscillations are sustained at the frequency at which the frequency-determining element or circuit is resonant.

Most oscillators deliver a sine wave signal (same as AC power line waveform). Others generate square waves, triangular waves, pulses, and other waveforms.

Output Devices

Some electronic devices require no output unit and are connected directly to the mechanism to be controlled. Others drive a relay, solenoid, or positioning device.

Power Supplies

All electronic devices require a source of electrical power. Generally, for industrial applications, the primary power source is the AC power line (115 or 230 volts). In most cases, the AC power must be converted to DC by a rectifier, which may be an external power supply or may be built into the device.

For tubes, the power supply delivers low voltage AC (usually 6.3 or 12.6 volts) to the tube heaters or filaments, and relatively high voltage DC (100 to 400 volts) to the plates and screens of the tubes. For transistors, the power supply delivers low voltage DC (3 to 40 volts) to the transistor elements. In some equipment, several independent DC power sources are provided for purposes of isolation.

• TRANSMISSION MEDIA

In electronics work, we deal with "signals" of relatively low, often miniscule power, which control substantial amounts of power, relatively speaking.

Signals may be transmitted from one location to another through a simple pair of wires, a telephone cable, a shielded cable (Fig. 157), a coaxial cable (Fig. 158) or via radio, depending on the level and nature of the signals. When low level signals are to be transmitted, either shielded or coaxial cable is often used in order to avoid pickup of hum, electrical noise, and other interfering signals.

Multiplexing

Ordinarily, a pair of wires is used for transmitting one signal in one direction. The capacity of a pair of wires can be increased by employing FDM (frequency division multiplex) or TDM (time division multiplex). In the former case (Fig. 159), several signals can be transmitted simultaneously in one or both directions. With TDM (Fig. 160), the transmission

CUT THE CABLE ACCORDING TO THE DIMENSIONS BELOW.
PREPARE EACH END AS SHOWN.

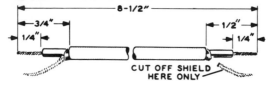

TAKING CARE NOT TO CUT THE OUTER SHIELD OF VERY
THIN WIRES, REMOVE THE OUTER INSULATION.

PUSH BACK THE SHIELD. THEN MAKE AN OPENING IN THE
SHIELD AND BEND OVER AS SHOWN. PICK OUT THE
INNER LEAD.

REMOVE THE INNER INSULATION AND STRETCH OUT
THE SHIELD. APPLY A SMALL AMOUNT OF SOLDER TO THE
END OF THE SHIELD AND THE INNER LEAD. USE ONLY
ENOUGH HEAT FOR THE SOLDER TO FLOW.

Fig. 157. Shielded cable and typical example of
preparation method (Courtesy of Heath
Co.).

139

Fig. 158. Coaxial cable.

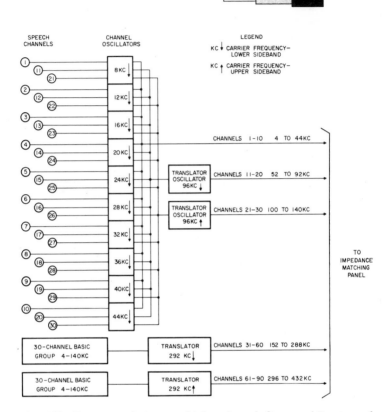

Fig. 159. Frequency division multiplex channel diagram (Courtesy of Stromberg-Carlson).

Fig. 160. Time division multiplex wave form (example of pulse amplitude modulation).

medium is capable of handling several signals on a time sharing basis.

FDM. In an FDM transmission system, the signals are transmitted over tone channels, each consisting of a tone generator (transmitter) and a tone receiver (Fig. 161). As many as 100 tone channels, each operating at a different frequency, can be transmitted over a wire line circuit which will handle frequencies between 300 Hz and 3000 Hz, when the equipment uses Twintrons as frequency determining elements and selection filters. With the use of LC frequency-determining elements and filters, about 30 tone channels can be accommodated.

Intelligence is transmitted by keying of the tone generator on and off, or by shifting of the frequency of the tone generator. At the tone receiver, a relay is energized or a DC voltage is produced when a tone signal is being received or shifted to a specific frequency.

Some tone generators are of the analog type. The output frequency is continuously variable within a specific band, and is determined by the level and polarity of the input signal. At the receiver, the output signal is a duplicate of the input signal.

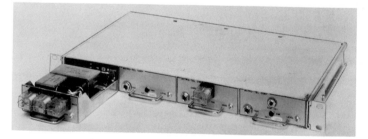

Fig. 161. Tone multiplex terminal employing plug-in transmitter, receiver, and power supply modules (Courtesy of Metro-tel Corp.).

TDM. In a TDM system, an electronic scanner encoder (Fig. 162) samples several input signal sources. When a signal is present, a DC pulse is transmitted. At the other end of

141

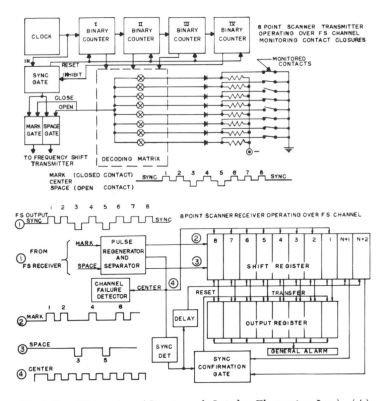

Fig. 162. TDM system (Courtesy of Quindar Electronics, Inc.). (A) Scan encoder (B) Scan decoder.

the circuit, a scanning decoder, operating in synchronism with the encoder, delivers an output signal to various circuits when their counterpart inputs have a signal present. This type of system enables one-way transmission over a wire line circuit. Two-way transmission can be made possible by the use of two tone channels, one for each direction. The output of each encoder is used to key its associated tone generator. The output of each tone receiver is fed to the input of its associated decoder. With the use of more tone channels, a number of TDM channels can be multiplexed on the same circuit.

142

Coaxial Cable

While not yet in wide use in industrial plants, coaxial cable is an almost ideal medium for communications, television, data and control-telemetering signal transmission. A single coaxial cable network is capable of handling numerous CCTV channels and telephone circuits, and thousands of signaling channels when multiplexed.

• SUMMARY

An electronic system may consist of a single piece of equipment or several devices, and may include subsystems. Each system component is seldom complex. It is the multiplicity of components that may make a system appear complex.

In electronic work, we deal with "signals," as opposed to power in electrical work. The signals may be AC or DC, analog (continuously variable) or digital (present or absent).

9 ⋮ Electronic System Maintenance

The ability to read electronic circuit symbols (see Chapter 1) is a basic requirement for servicing electronic equipment. Block diagrams are used to make it easy to visualize system operation. Schematic diagrams show the actual electrical circuits. Wiring diagrams show the physical circuit arrangements.

• TEST EQUIPMENT

The availability of adequate test equipment is another basic requirement (see Table 5). Equipment employing plug-in modules (Fig. 163) can be serviced without test

Table 5

BASIC ELECTRONIC TEST EQUIPMENT

Instrument	Functions	Applications
VOM (volt-ohm-milliammeter)	Measures DC and AC voltages and currents; also ohms.	General troubleshooting and low impedance/low frequency circuit signal level measurements.

VTVM (vacuum tube voltmeter)	Measures AC and DC voltages.	Signal tracing and measurements in high impedance circuits.
Oscilloscope	Displays electrical waveforms and voltage.	Troubleshooting, signal tracing and waveform observation.
Electronic Counter	Measures frequency and number of events.	Frequency measurements and counting.
AF Signal Generator	Generates AF signals from 20 Hz to 20 KHz or higher.	Test signal source.
RF Signal Generator	Generates RF signals. (Available in many ranges).	Test signal source for radio equipment.
Tube Tester	Checks tubes for defects and relative merit.	Troubleshooting and preventive maintenance.
Transistor Tester (in-circuit type)	Checks transistors for defects and gain.	Troubleshooting.

equipment by simple testing with spare modules; defective modules can be sent back to the manufacturer for repair. But there are many instances requiring the use of test equipment for troubleshooting. Often the trouble is in interconnection wiring and external devices.

• VOM

A volt-ohm-milliammeter (VOM) is the most essential servicing tool. It permits measurement of AC and DC voltage, current, and resistance. A typical VOM (Fig. 164) is equipped with numerous measurement ranges. Since a VOM requires

145

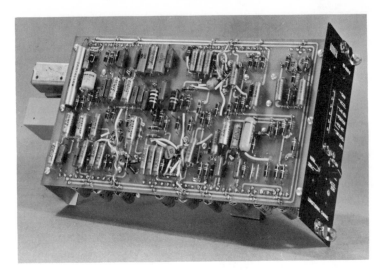

Fig. 163. Plug-in module (Courtesy of Systron-Donner Corp.).

Fig. 164. Typical volt-ohm-milliammeter.

no electrical power, except from a self-contained battery for resistance measurements, it is fully portable and can be used anywhere. For electronics work, the VOM should be of the 20,000-ohms-per-volt (or higher) type.

• VTVM

A vacuum tube voltmeter (VTVM) is also an essential tool. Many of them provide the same functions as a VOM, but they have a very high input resistance (several megohms). This feature is important. A VTVM can be used to measure voltages in circuits where the loading effect of a VOM would provide misleading readings. A typical VTVM is shown in Fig. 165.

While the AC voltage indications of a VOM are accurate only at power and audio frequencies, a typical VTVM is quite accurate at frequencies up to several megacycles. The frequency range can be expanded further with the use of a low capacity probe or an RF probe, which rectifies the measured AC voltage so that it can be measured as DC.

Fig. 165. Vacuum tube voltmeter.

Electronic Voltmeter

An electronic voltmeter (Fig. 166) is similar to a VTVM, but employs transistors instead of tubes. Whereas a VTVM usually must be connected to a power line, an electronic voltmeter operates from self-contained batteries.

Fig. 166. Electronic voltmeter.

Oscilloscope

This is the most useful measuring device of all, but its use requires skill. An oscilloscope (Fig. 167) can be used for measuring voltage, current, power, frequency, phase shift, modulation level, and distortion. It is essentially a voltmeter with a cathode ray tube (CRT) as an indicator. The voltage is proportional to vertical deflection of the electron beam. The electron beam is also swept horizontally across the screen of the CRT by an internal sawtooth wave generator. By variation of the sweep rate, voltage with respect to time can be measured.

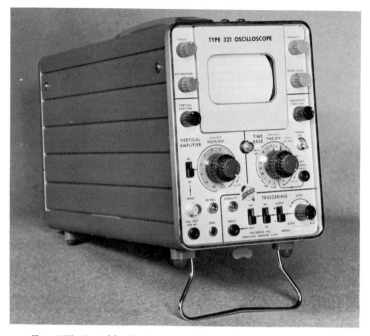

Fig. 167. Portable, battery-operated oscilloscope. Since it is
independent of power lines, it is particularly useful
in electronic systems maintenance.

For example, when the sweep rate is 60 Hz (cycles per second), and a 60 Hz signal is measured, the waveform of one cycle will appear on the CRT screen, as shown in Fig. 168. With reduction of the sweep rate to 30 Hz, two complete cycles can be observed. The typical, low cost oscilloscope can be adjusted to sweep at rates up to 100,000 times per second, making it possible to observe waveforms of signals at frequencies up to several megahertz (above 100 Hz, more than one cycle will appear).

Since the actual waveform can be observed, distortion can be detected. An oscilloscope can also be used for detecting the presence of noise and intermodulation. To get maximum benefit from an oscilloscope, one should read one of the several available books on the use of oscilloscopes.

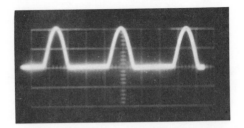

Fig. 168. Waveform of a half-wave rectified AC voltage as seen on the
screen of an oscilloscope.

Electronic Counter

This is a time-saving tool. While fairly expensive, an electronic counter (see Fig. 144) can often pay for itself quickly through time savings, both of personnel and equipment downtime. An electronic counter displays frequency, count tally, and events-per-unit of time in illuminated numerals. In electronics maintenance work, it provides quick, precise measurement of signal frequencies.

Sine/Square Wave Generator

When AC and AF signals are involved, an AF signal generator can be used as a source of test signals. Most AF signal generators can be tuned to any frequency between 20 Hz and 20 KHz. Some deliver only a sine wave signal (Fig. 169), while others deliver either a sine wave or square wave signal (Fig. 170), as selected by a front panel switch.

RF Signal Generator

An RF signal generator (Fig. 171) is required only in maintaining equipment utilizing signals at frequencies above 100 KHz (radio and wireless intercom, for example). Numerous models of RF signal generators are on the market, ranging in cost from 25 to several thousand dollars. A low-cost type will suffice for troubleshooting. But for calibration purposes, only a laboratory grade instrument should be considered.

Fig. 169. Sine wave generator (Courtesy of Systron-Donner Corp.).

Fig. 170. Audio frequency signal generator for producing sine or square waves (Courtesy of Allied Radio Corporation).

151

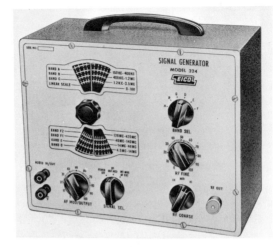

Fig. 171. RF signal generator.

Fig. 172. Typical tube tester (Courtesy of Heath Co.).

Other test units required for electronics maintenance work include the tube tester (Fig. 172) and the in-circuit transistor checker (Fig. 173).

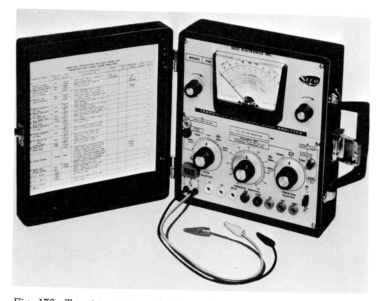

Fig. 173. Transistor tester which can be used for testing transistors without removing them from the equipment (Courtesy of Seco Electronics, Inc.).

• PERSONNEL

An electrician should be able to maintain electronic equipment without extensive retraining if he has a firm understanding of electrical theory. While this book does not attempt to cover electronics theory in depth, it does provide basic information without confusion. Those interested in learning more about electronics theory will find several excellent books on the subject available at electronics parts distributors and technical book stores. There are also excellent home study courses.

Maintenance of radio transmitters should be performed only by a person possessing a second class radiotelephone operator license, or a person working under the supervision of a licensed man, as required by the FCC Rules and Regulations.

• PREVENTIVE MAINTENANCE

Downtime can be minimized by the application of preventive maintenance. Most important of all is keeping electronic equipment clean. Film and dirt retard heat dissipation. Heat is the enemy of electronic equipment and tends to shorten the life of components. Equipment can be cleaned with a gentle blast of air and by using an acceptable cleaning solvent (not carbon tetrachloride).

In equipment employing tubes, the tubes should be tested at least once every 90 days; weak or otherwise defective tubes should be replaced. There is no need to test transistors unless the equipment fails, since transistors are either good or no good at all.

Relay and switch contacts can be cleaned with a solvent or contact burnishing tool, but never with a file or sandpaper. Plug-in connectors should be inspected and cleaned periodically.

• TROUBLESHOOTING

Locating the cause of trouble often requires more time than performing repairs. Table 6 is a basic troubleshoot-

Table 6

BASIC TROUBLESHOOTING TECHNIQUES

Sympton	What to Check	How to Check
No Operation	Presence of electric power	With voltmeter or test lamp.
	Fuse	Try new fuse.
	Short circuit in equipment	Measure input current with ammeter.

No Output Signal (power present)	Presence of input signal	At input with VTVM or oscilloscope.
	Signal path through equipment	Apply test signal at input and check for signal at output with VTVM or oscilloscope.
Instability	Improper power voltage	With voltmeter.
	Interference at input	With oscilloscope at input.
	Defect within equipment	Try spare.
Intermittent Operation	Input, output, and power connections	Visual inspection.
	Defect within equipment	Try spare.
	Defective input device	Apply test signal and observe output with VTVM or oscilloscope.
	Defective output device	Replace output device with dummy load and observe output signal with VTVM or oscilloscope.
Poor Accuracy	Defect within equipment	Apply test signals, observe output with VTVM or oscilloscope, and compare with specifications.

ing chart. Troubleshooting is confined to checking for the presence of signals at the input and output of each system component, and determination of failure in a power supply. If an input signal is present and there is no output signal, it is obvious that the trouble is within the device being checked.

In order to minimize downtime, spare system components should be available for use while the defective device is being repaired.

• REPAIRS

A well-equipped shop is required for repairing system components. Jigs may be required to enable bench operation of plug-in modules.

Great care should be exercised in removing or installing transistors and diodes with a soldering iron. A low-wattage soldering iron should be used, and the transistor or diode lead should be held firmly with pliers to minimize heating of the semiconductor.

Replacement Parts

Ordinarily, spare parts are available from the equipment manufacturer. Standard parts, such as resistors, capacitors, tubes, transistors, and diodes, can usually be purchased at much lower prices from electronic parts distributors. Special parts, obviously, must be obtained from the manufacturer or distributor.

• SUMMARY

Adequate test equipment and spares are required for maintaining electronic equipment and in order to minimize system downtime. Information on the use of test equipment is usually provided with the equipment. Specific information on troubleshooting is usually provided in the service manuals furnished with electronic equipment.

10 : Electronic
  : Devices
  : And
  : Circuits

This chapter describes numerous electronic devices and circuits, and defines terms used in electronics, in alphabetical
order.

ADP (Automatic Data Processing). This term refers to data
processing performed by a system of electronic or electrical
machines so interconnected as to negate as much as possible
the need for human work.

AC-DC. An AC-DC electronic device is operable from
either AC or DC (of the same voltage) without modification.
The AC-DC radio, introduced by Barnet Trott, substantially
reduced the cost of radios, since a power transformer is not
required.

AF (Audio Frequency). The audio frequency range is usually associated with the hearing abilities of the human ear.
This frequency range is between approximately 50 Hz and
20,000 Hz, although it is a fact that both extremes are often
beyond the hearing capabilities of most people.

AFC (Automatic Frequency Control). An electronic circuit
employed to insure that another electronic circuit will not
change its frequency. AFC automatically compensates for
changes which tend to cause the frequency of an oscillator or
generator to vary.

AGC (Automatic Gain Control). A circuit employed in electronic devices to change the amount of amplification in order to maintain constant output level. In radio receivers, it is used to control the gain of both the RF and IF stages so that variations in input level will not change the output level (Fig. 174).

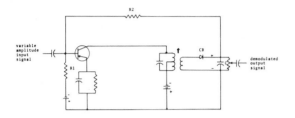

Fig. 174. AGC circuit. The base of the transistor is forward biased through R1. The transistor's output signal is rectified by diode CR, charging C in the polarity indicated. As the signal level tends to rise, the positive voltage across C rises and is fed through R2 to the transistor base reducing its forward bias, rise, and, hence, its gain.

Algol (Algorithmic Language). A data processing language used to express problem-solving formulas for solution by machines.

Alpha. A term used to indicate the current gain of a transistor in a common base circuit. There are two alphas that are measured. One is the dynamic AC alpha, and the other is a static DC alpha.

AM (Amplitude Modulation). A method of transmitting intelligence by varying the amplitude of a carrier signal. All standard radio broadcast stations operating in the 540 to 1600 KHz band employ AM.

Amphenol Connector. A mechanical device used to make electrical connections between two chassis or cabinets; it can be disconnected quickly. It usually is used to permit a quick disconnect of circuits without the need of soldering or unsoldering. These connectors come as male and female units and can be made to accommodate a large number of electrical circuits.

Amplification. Term used to indicate how much amplification (gain) a tube or transistor provides or is capable of providing. The amount of amplification is usually expressed in terms of either voltage or db (decibels).

Amplification Factor. This term usually is associated with vacuum tubes and is expressed by the unit mu. It is a measure of the relative effectiveness of voltages on electrodes within the tube.

Amplifier, AF (Amplifier, Audio Frequency). An amplifier used to amplify audio frequencies only. It should not only amplify, but be able to reproduce faithfully all information (audio frequencies) put into it, with a minimum of distortion. (See Fig. 153.)

Amplifier, Cascade. This term means just what it says. Two, three, or more amplifier stages are connected in cascade, one feeding the other. The reasons are obvious. If each stage can provide a gain of 10, then two stages can provide a gain of 100. For example: one stage = gain of 10. The second stage starts with the gain of 10 from the first stage and then multiplies that by 10, giving a total gain of 100 (Fig. 175).

Fig. 175. Cascaded amplifier stages.

Amplifier, Class A. This is usually an amplifier stage designed to reproduce faithfully at its output an almost exact duplicate of what went in. Distortion is very low.

Amplifier, Class B. This is usually an AF amplifier stage that is designed to provide more power output than a Class A amplifier. Its one disadvantage is that distortion is quite high.

Amplifier, Class C. This is an amplifier that is designed for amplification of radio frequencies. High efficiency is obtained.

159

Distortion is minimized when the output is connected to a resonant circuit.

Amplifier, DC (**Amplifier, Direct Current**). An amplifier capable of amplifying signals that are either AC or DC. It is used in many industrial circuits. A typical application is strain measurement, where the input signal is obtained from a resistive strain gauge excited by DC. (See Fig. 152.)

Amplifier, Grounded Grid. This is an amplifier that is designed for amplification of radio frequencies. It is wired so that the control grid is grounded and the signal is fed into the cathode (or filament). The advantage is that neutralization is not needed (Fig. 176).

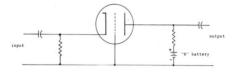

input   output

"B" battery

Fig. 176. Grounded grid amplifier.

Amplifier, IF (**Amplifier, Intermediate Frequency**). This is an amplifier employed in superheterodyne radio receivers. The IF stages are used to amplify the radio frequency signals after frequency translation (Fig. 177).

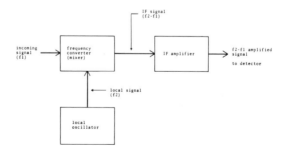

Fig. 177. Basic superheterodyne circuit.

Amplifier, Linear. The term is self-explanatory. An amplifier that amplifies in a linear manner (like a Class A amplifier), reproducing the input signal faithfully.

Amplifier, Magnetic. An electrical device which uses saturable reactors, either by themselves, or with other components to obtain amplification or control (Fig. 178).

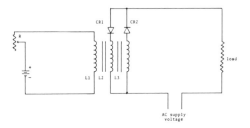

Fig. 178. Simple magnetic amplifier. Load current flows during one half-cycle through L2 and CR1 and during the the other half-cycle through L3 and CR2. The reactance at L2 and L3 is controlled by the DC flowing through control winding L1. Hence, adjustment of R controls load current and voltage.

Amplifier, Push-Pull. An amplifier stage in which two tubes or transistors are employed for amplification. They are usually operated so that each tube alternates with the other continuously to obtain more linear output. The grids of the tubes, or bases of the transistors, are fed signals 180 degrees out of phase with each other. Figure 179 shows the difference between a single-ended and a push-pull amplifier.

Amplifier, RF (Amplifier, Radio Frequency). An amplifier designed specifically to amplify signals at radio frequencies.

Amplifier, Servo. This is an amplifier used as part of a servomechanism system. A servomechanism system is used for electronic control of mechanical devices. (See Fig. 133.)

Amplifier, Transistor. An amplifier utilizing a transistor instead of a tube.

161

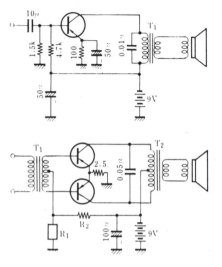

Fig. 179. (A) Simple-ended amplifier.
(B) Push-pull amplifier.
(Courtesy of Hitachi, Ltd.).

Amplifier, Vacuum Tube. An amplifier utilizing a vacuum tube to provide amplification.

Analog. This term is used in computer work. An analog computer (Fig. 180) uses stepless changes as input data and indicates the significance such changes have on the device or unit as a whole. The output accuracy of this type computer is "analogous" to the accuracy of the input data.

"And" Circuit. If two or more gates are placed in series, the result is known as an "AND" gate. There are many variations that can be utilized to set up an "AND" function. The basic circuit operates so that voltage is present at the output. To cut off the output voltage, both gates must be open. This is done by triggering of both gates simultaneously. Or the gates can both be opened and closed by triggering of both gates simultaneously. Figure 181 illustrates the principle of an "AND" circuit.

162

Fig. 180. Analog computer (Courtesy of Systron-Donner Corp.).

Fig. 181. Circuit for demonstrating
"AND" principle. Voltage
is applied to the load only
when both S1 and S2 are
closed.

ASA Code. An information-interchange, seven-level code adopted as a standard code by the American Standards Association.

Attenuator. This is a device, either a potentiometer or a switch (wired up with various resistances across it), that is used to provide attenuation. The potentiometer provides a smooth change. The switch provides attenuation in steps (Fig. 182).

163

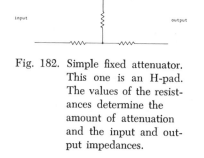

Fig. 182. Simple fixed attenuator.
This one is an H-pad.
The values of the resist-
ances determine the
amount of attenuation
and the input and out-
put impedances.

Audio. A term used to indicate frequencies to which the human ear can ordinarily respond (between 50 Hz to 20,000 Hz).

Audion. The original term used to identify a triode vacuum tube.

Autodyne Converter. A frequency converter, employing a single tube or transistor, that functions as both a local oscillator and a mixer. The output frequency is equal to the sum or difference of the external input signal and the local oscillator signal. (See Fig. 130.)

Autotransformer. This is a transformer that has only one winding. The winding has various taps on it. The input voltage is placed across one part of the winding, which functions as the primary, and various voltages are made available through the use of the taps. The voltages available are either higher or lower than the source. Figure 183 is a schematic of

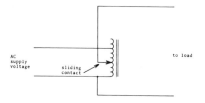

Fig. 183. Continuously variable autotransformer enables raising or lowering of line
voltage.

a continuously variable autotransformer for raising or lowering AC line voltage.

AVC (**Automatic Volume Control**). A circuit utilized in radio receivers to reduce or eliminate fading or overloading. Fading would cause this signal to vary from strong to very weak. Overloading would cause distortion and unintelligible intelligence. The AVC senses input signal level and automatically adjusts gain to provide a constant level output signal. (See AGC.)

B—. Term used to indicate a negative voltage in power supplies.

B+. Term used to indicate positive DC voltage available for use in electronic equipment. This voltage is fed to plates and screens of tubes or collectors of NPN transistors. In some schematic diagrams, the actual power source is not shown. Instead, the circuits connected to the power source are labeled "B+," "B—," or "C—," as illustrated in Fig. 184.

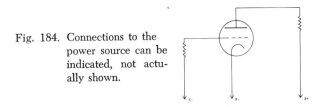

Fig. 184. Connections to the power source can be indicated, not actually shown.

Battery (**A**). A dry or wet cell or battery the primary use of which is supplying filament voltage for tubes.

Battery (**B**). A group of dry cells or wet cells arranged to form a relatively high voltage battery (22.5 to 135 volts) specifically designed to supply voltage for plates and screens of tubes.

Baud. A unit of digital signaling speed equal to the number of code elements per second. It is used interchangeably with "bits per second" as the unit of measure of data flow.

Bias. An electrical potential difference that does not vary; it is used across given elements of a tube or transistor to set its operating parameters.

Bias, Cathode. A non-varying potential difference which is derived from the voltage developed across the cathode resistor of a vacuum tube, due to cathode current flow. Since the voltage at the cathode is positive with respect to the grid, the grid is negatively biased. (See Fig. 83.)

Bias, Fixed. A non-varying potential difference that is derived from a separate source. This negative DC voltage is usually obtained from a battery or rectifier. (See Fig. 82.)

Bias, Grid Leak. A non-varying potential difference which is developed across an R-C combination in the grid circuit of a vacuum tube. A negative DC voltage is developed at the grid because of the rectifying action of the grid and cathode when a positive signal is applied to the grid. (See Fig. 90.)

BIM (Beginning of Information Marker). A reflective spot on the back of a magnetic tape, 10 feet from the physical beginning of the tape, which, when electrically sensed, indicates the point on the tape for the recording to start.

Bleeder. A resistor that is wired across the output of a DC power supply. This resistor is designed to discharge the voltage rapidly after the power is shut off. It also helps stabilize the DC output voltage.

Boolean Logic. A mathematical analysis of logic. It includes information retrieval and circuit switching designs, and is derived from a process used in algebra formulated by George Boole.

BTU. A unit of work or energy: the energy required to raise the temperature of one pound of water one degree Fahrenheit is equal to one British Thermal Unit.

C—. Usually refers to a bias voltage. In this case, it is called a negative bias voltage, and is used to control a vacuum tube. (See Fig. 184.)

Cable, Coaxial. A round, shielded cable using a polyethylene material inside of which is a copper wire. This kind of cable is used between transmitters or receivers and their antenna or for direct transmission of video or radio frequency signals. Coaxial cable is used because it has low losses, does not deteriorate readily, and cuts down or eliminates interference because its inner conductor is shielded. (See Fig. 158.)

Cable, Shielded. A cable which has a shield on the outside, insulated from its internal conductors. This kind of cable is used to reduce noise pickup when the circuits it carries have to be kept free of outside influence. (See Fig. 157.)

Cable, Twin Lead. A cable used as a transmission line for television and FM radio receivers. It is made up of two conductors, spaced approximately one-half inch apart with a plastic material as a spacer between them. The plastic completely encompasses the wires to make the cable waterproof (Fig. 185).

Fig. 185. Twin-lead cable. Two conductors are separated from each other and insulated, molded inside a flat plastic strip.

Cannon Connector. This is the name given to a mechanical plug or socket combination manufactured by Cannon. These plugs and sockets are available in a variety of contact arrangements to accommodate different types, sizes, and numbers of wires.

Capacitor. An electrical non-conductor that permits an electrical charge to be stored in it. This charge takes place as a result of electron displacement when opposite sides of the capacitor are kept at difference of potential. There are many types of capacitors used in electronic equipment.

Capacitor, Bypass. A bypass capacitor shunts to ground all unwanted signals, hash, etc., while at the same time permitting a DC potential to exist across it (Fig. 186).

Capacitor, Ceramic. This type of capacitor employs a ceramic material as the dielectric (Fig. 187).

Capacitor Defects. A capacitor (all types except electrolytic) can become shorted, open, or leaky. An electrolytic

167

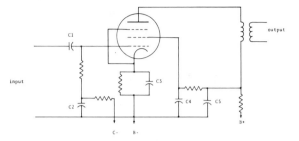

Fig. 186. Bypass capacitors. Capacitors C2, C3, C4, and
C5 bypass the signals to common ground but
do not short the DC operating voltages. Capacitor C1 is a "coupling" capacitor which
passes the signal, but blocks DC.

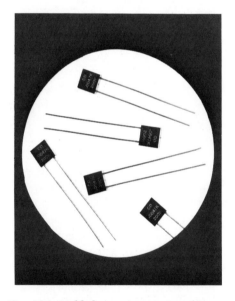

Fig. 187. Molded ceramic capacitors (Courtesy of Cornell-Dubilier Electronics).

capacitor can become less capacitive as its moist dielectric becomes dehydrated.

Capacitor, Disc. These capacitors usually employ ceramic as the dielectric, and the term "disc" is used to identify the physical shape (Fig. 188).

Capacitor, Electrolytic. These capacitors use an electrolyte as the dielectric. The capacitor has a chemical formed on the plates (usually made of aluminum), which are kept in a moist state. They are sealed so that dehydration does not take place. Because they have very large capacitance for their physical size, they are used primarily as filters in power supplies (Fig. 189).

Capacitor, Fixed. A capacitor which has a fixed value of capacitance. There are many types of fixed capacitances, such as mica, paper, electrolytic, ceramic, and so on.

Capacitor, Leakage. A capacitor is not supposed to have leakage. The only type which normally exhibits some leakage

Fig. 188 Disc capacitor.

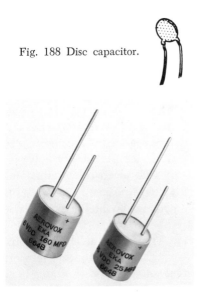

Fig. 189. Electrolytic capacitors.

is the electrolytic variety. No other capacitor should have leakage.

Capacitor, Mica. This type of capacitor uses mica as the dielectric material.

Capacitor, Mylar. This type of capacitor employs mylar (polyethylene terraphate) or a paper-mylar (plastic) combination as the dielectric.

Capacitor, Paper. This type of capacitor employs as its dielectric a paper that is sandwiched between two sheets of tinfoil. (See Fig. 41.)

Capacitor, Tantalum. This type of capacitor employs tantalum in place of aluminum; it is used where space and reliability are major considerations.

Capacitor, Trimmer. This is a variable capacitor the capacity of which is determined by a screw adjustment. Alternate layers of mica and tin plates are mounted on a plate. A hole is drilled through the center of these plates, and a threaded screw is turned either to loosen or compress the space between the mica and tin to vary the capacitance. There are also piston and other types of trimmer capacitors. (See Fig. 47.)

Capacitor, Variable. This type of capacitor generally employs air as the dielectric. Two sections of plates are interwoven, without touching each other. One of these sets of plates is rotatable, making possible changes in its physical position in relation to the fixed plates. This action varies the capacity. The more plates, the higher the capacity. (See Fig. 46.)

Card Reader. A device that senses holes in punched cards and converts them into electrical information.

Carrier. This is a term used to define a radio frequency or other signal that contains no intelligence unless it is modulated. (See Fig. 88.)

Carrier Current Transmission. This is a form of radio transmission employing wires as the transmission medium. The wires may be used solely for this purpose, or may be an existing telephone or power line in normal service. Carrier current transmission takes place at a frequency so high that no mutual

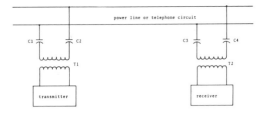

Fig. 190. Carrier current system. The transmitter
and receiver operate at a higher frequency than the electrical power or
telephone circuit to avoid mutual interference. Coupling to the line is through
impedance matching networks.

interference is caused to telephone service or power line operation. Thus, in a plant, the power lines can be used for
communications or signal transmission (Fig. 190).

Cathode Follower. An amplifier stage employing a tube
with plate at ground potential at the signal frequency (plate
is at a positive DC potential). The input signal is fed to the
grid, and the output signal is developed across the cathode
resistor. The input impedance is high, and the output impedance is low. The voltage gain is less than one. The input
and output signals are in phase, and not 180 degrees out of
phase with each other, as is the case when the output signal
is obtained at the plate. (See Fig. 85.)

Cathode Ray Tube. An electronic display tube, such as
those used in television receivers and oscilloscopes. An electron beam is projected to the tube's phosphor-coated screen,
causing an illuminated spot to appear at the point of impact
with the screen. The position of the spot can be moved by
application of voltages to vertical and horizontal deflection
plates. In television picture tubes, the beam is deflected mag-
netically by coils at the neck of the tube (Fig. 191).

CATV (Community Antenna Television). A system for dis-
tributing television and FM radio broadcast programs through-
out a community through a coaxial cable network. The signals
are picked up by antennas at the head end, where they are

171

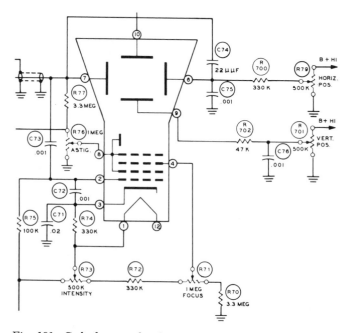

Fig. 191. Cathode ray tube showing basic circuitry (Courtesy of Heath Co.).

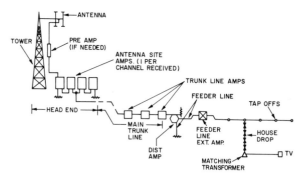

Fig. 192. CATV system diagram.

amplified and fed into a trunk line cable. The trunk line is connected to feeder cables, which in turn feed distribution cables that are tapped by subscriber drops. Line amplifiers

172

are employed at intervals to offset transmission losses in the cables (Fig. 192).

CCTV (Closed Circuit Television). A television system using wire or cable as the transmission medium (Fig. 193).

Charactron. A special type of cathode ray tube capable of displaying various characters and symbols on its screen, and usually used for observation of information (Fig. 194).

Fig. 193. Block diagram of closed circuit television system.

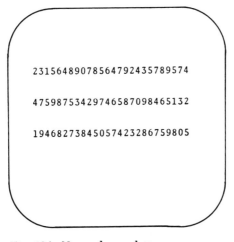

Fig. 194. Numerals or letters appear on screen of charactron.

Chassis. A metallic box or shelf on which electronic components are mounted. The chassis is often employed as the common ground circuit. In some cases, the chassis is electrically isolated from the circuitry.

173

Choke, Filter. A reactor made up of a laminated iron core on which is wound many turns of copper wire. The name "filter" is given to it because of its use. It is used in power supplies in conjunction with capacitors to form a low pass filter that removes the ripple from the output of a rectifier. (See Fig. 57.)

Choke, RF (Choke, Radio Frequency). This is a coil made up of many turns of insulated wire wound in a single layer or in banks on a ceramic form. Its purpose is to permit DC to pass through it unopposed, and to oppose passage of radio frequencies. (See Fig. 54.)

Choke, Swinging. An automatically variable inductance reactor used in the input section of a two-stage power supply filter. The adjustment of the air gap in the cone determines how well it can change its inductance with varying load.

Citizens Band. A band of radio frequencies divided into channels for use by licensees in the Citizens Radio Service for business and personal communications or remote control of devices. There are two citizens bands, one between 26.96 MHz and 27.26 MHz, the other within the 460 to 470 MHz band. Figure 195 shows a typical citizens band radio transceiver.

Fig. 195. Citizens radio transceiver (Courtesy of Allied Radio Corporation).

Clipper. An electronic circuit designed to clip or cut off any electrical signal voltage either below or above a certain predetermined level. (See Fig. 60.)

Coaxial Cable. See Cable, Coaxial.

COBOL (Common Business Oriented Language). A specific language designed for commercial data processing as developed and defined by a national committee of computer manufacturers and users.

Code, International Morse. A dot-dash code used by telegraph and wireless operators of all countries (except U.S. land line telegraph operators, who use American Morse code).

Color Code, Capacitor. The color code on some capacitors indicates to the user capacity, voltage rating, and tolerance. Since most capacitors are too small to contain all of the above information, color bands or dots are used to indicate this information. (See Fig. 42.)

Color Code, Resistor. This color code is banded around a resistor to indicate its resistance and tolerance. Since most resistors are too small to contain these values, a color coding system was devised. (See Fig. 17.)

Color Code, Transformer. Transformer leads are color coded to enable the user to determine the winding information. Some transformers have 15 to 20 leads, and it would be very difficult to prepare a chart indicating the necessary information (Fig. 196).

Converter. A device for converting DC to AC (see inverter), or AC to DC, for increasing or decreasing DC voltage, or for translating one frequency to another. The circuit of a DC-to-DC inverter is shown in Fig. 197.

Coupling, RC (Coupling, Resistance-Capacitance). A resistor-capacitor combination wired to permit AC signals to pass through but to block DC voltage. (See Fig. 82.)

Coupling, Transformer. A transformer is used between two stages. It provides a means of changing impedance without significant power loss. It can also be used to transfer a signal from one stage to another efficiently and to step the voltage up or down. The primary is usually connected to the plate

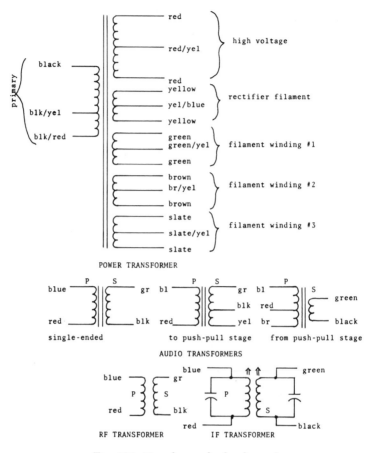

Fig. 196. Transformer lead color code.

circuit of a tube and the secondary to the grid circuit of the next stage. In a transistor circuit, the primary is usually connected to the collector and the secondary to the base of the next transistor. (See Fig. 86.)

Cryogenics. The study and use of devices utilizing the properties of materials near absolute zero in temperature.

Crystal Detector. A diode detector that demodulates AM signals through rectifying action. (See Fig. 58.)

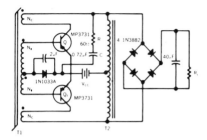

Fig. 197. DC-to-DC inverter (Courtesy of Motorola Semiconductor Products, Inc.).

Fig. 198. Crystal diode conducts current in only one direction. The crystal rectifier was once used only in simple radio receivers. Now it is a very important component of computers, radar, and control systems.

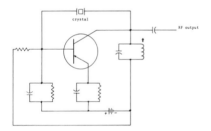

Fig. 199. Crystal-controlled oscillator.

Fig. 200. Quartz crystal.

177

Crystal Diode. A device that utilizes silicon or another semiconductor substance. This device can be used as a detector, gate, rectifier, switch, clipper, and so on (Fig. 198).

Crystal Oscillator. A circuit designed to generate a radio frequency using a piezoelectric crystal as its frequency-determining element. This oscillator is very stable and can withstand changes in voltage and temperature without significant effects on frequency (Fig. 199).

Crystal, Quartz. A crystal made of quartz used in transmitters and receiver oscillators as the frequency-determining element (Fig. 200).

Cut-Off-Bias. A term used to describe the bias voltage necessary to cut off a tube or transistor. To cut off means to stop from conducting.

Data Conversion. The process of changing information from one form to another, for example, from magnetic tape to the printed page.

Decade. A group or assembly of ten units. It can consist of a counter that counts to 10 in one column or a resistor box that utilizes resistors in multiples of powers of 10 (Fig. 201).

Decoder. A device for decoding coded signals. Some are responsive to audio tone frequencies or to DC pulses coded by variation of their duration, spacing, or number. Usually, the output of a decoder is a DC voltage or relay contact closure (Fig. 202).

Destructive Read. A process that takes information from a storage device and, in so doing, destroys the information stored in that device.

Detector, AM (Detector, Amplitude Modulation). A demodulator of amplitude-modulated signals. It is a nonlinear device and may consist of a diode and transistor or tube, biased so that it operates in the nonlinear portion of its characteristics curve (Fig. 203).

Detector, FM (Detector, Frequency Modulation). A demodulator for frequency-modulated signals. There are several types of FM detectors. One is called a ratio detector, and another is called a discriminator. In the discriminator circuit

178

Fig. 201. Decade box.

Fig. 202. Secode decoder (at right) responds to pulses produced
by a telephone dial (at left).

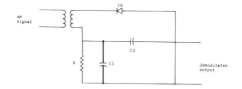

Fig. 203. AM detector employing a diode. The signal is rectified by diode CR. The demodulated signal is developed across R and derived through C2; C1 bypasses unwanted carrier signals.

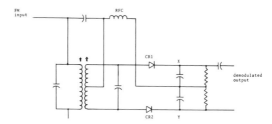

Fig. 204. Foster-Seeley discriminator. Voltage across X and Y is zero when input signal is not modulated (carrier only). As signal frequency varies, voltage at X and Y, its amplitude depending on the amount of frequency deviation, its polarity or direction of frequency deviation, and its frequency on the modulating frequency.

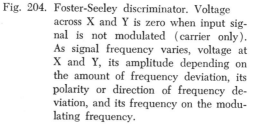

(Fig. 204), the output is derived from the rectified differences of the two voltages produced across two resonant circuits, one circuit tuned slightly below, and the other slightly above the carrier frequency. In the ratio detector circuit (Fig. 205), the ratio of two voltages of differing frequency produces an output signal the amplitude of which is a function of frequency difference. Still another type of FM detector employs a gated beam tube in which the phase relationship of the signals at its control and quadrature grids determines the amplitude of the output signal. (See Fig. 114.)

180

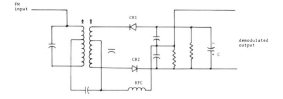

Fig. 205. One version of a ratio detector. Demodulated signal is developed across R.
Capacitor C charges to a level determined by input signal amplitude and
tends to nullify effects of amplitude
variations.

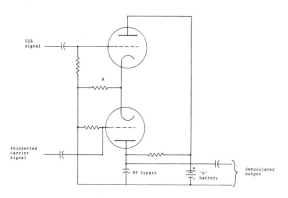

Fig. 206. One type of product detector. Coupling between the two triodes is via R.

Detector, Infinite Impedance. A detector in which the output is taken from the cathode circuit. The grid, being negative
at all times, draws no current. It has high input impedance
and introduces negligible distortion. (See Fig. 91.)

Detector, Product. A detector the output of which is the
product of two inputs. In an SSB radio receiver, one signal is
from the station being received, and the other is from a local
oscillator at the carrier frequency (Fig. 206).

Detector, SSB (Detector, Single Sideband). A detector used
for single sideband reception. Since no carrier is present, an

181

ordinary AM detector will not demodulate SSB signals. A detector, such as the product detector, is ideal for this purpose. (See Detector, Product.)

Diode. A term used to describe any two-element electronic device that ordinarily permits current to pass through it in one direction only. It can be a tube or semiconductor device.

Diode, Semiconductor. Semiconductor made up of a P and N type material. When they are placed together, the combination acts as a diode. Hence, it will rectify. Often called P-N junction diodes.

Diode, Thermionic. A tube which has only two elements, a cathode (or filament) and anode (plate).

Diode, Zener. A diode used as a voltage regulator. It has the ability to correct for variations of current, thus maintaining constant the voltage across a circuit. The current flowing through it varies, but the voltage across it remains constant. (See Fig. 68.)

Disk Files. A storage medium that consists of numbers of disks that rotate; each disk has a special magnetic coating that is used to store information.

Driver Stage. An amplifier stage used to supply enough signal power to the final amplifier stage so that it can operate at maximum power or efficiency.

DSB (Double Sideband). All AM and FM transmitters generate a carrier with two sidebands, upper and lower. Since both sidebands carry the same information, it is not necessary to transmit both sidebands.

Duplex. Usually refers to a signal channel capable of simultaneous transmission in both directions.

Earphone. A device that converts electrical current changes into audible sound. Most earphones employ an electromagnet and a metal diaphragm. Some employ a piezoelectric crystal that flexes with variations in applied voltage.

Eddy Current. Undesirable currents that flow in a transformer because of flux leakage. It contributes to power losses in magnetic materials, the shield and even the conductors themselves.

182

Elcell. An atomic battery invented by Cyril Elwell.

Electron. A negatively charged particle which is attracted to positively charged objects.

Electron Eye. A tube that indicates voltage level on a green screen; it has the appearance of an eye. Used to indicate signal levels in tape recorders, radio receivers, and so on. (See Fig. 107.)

Elevator Coil. This term is sometimes used to describe the impedance matching, input transformer used with a radio or television receiver. It is also called a balun (Fig. 207).

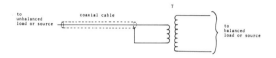

Fig. 207. Principle of a balun. A balun permits
the matching of impedances and a balanced circuit to an unbalanced circuit.

emf (Electromotive Force). This is an electrical potential difference across the terminals of a source of electricity. It is also called voltage and is expressed by the letter "E."

Erase Head. A device used in tape recorders to erase previous information on tape before the recording of new information.

Error. A general term indicating any deviation of a computed or measured quantity from the true or correct value.

Facsimile. A method of transmitting graphic material over wires or radio. The material to be transmitted is scanned photoelectrically and reproduced electrochemically.

Farad. The unit of capacitance. A farad is the capacitance of a capacitor that charges up to one coulomb when one volt is placed across its terminals. Actually, this is a tremendous quantity. Most capacitors are rated in microfarads and picofarads.

FDM. Abbreviation for frequency division multiplex (Fig. 208).

FET. Abbreviation for field effect transistor (Fig. 209).

Fig. 208. FDM multiplex terminal (Courtesy of General Electric Co.).

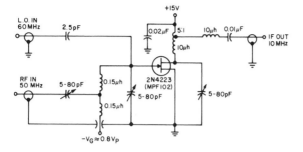

Fig. 209. Frequency converter employing a field effect transistor (FET). (Courtesy of Motorola Semiconductor Products, Inc.).

Filter, L-C. A filter network made up of L and C (inductance and capacitance).

Filter, R-C. A filter network made up of R and C (resistance and capacitance).

Flip-Chip. A new kind of digital system module which consists of encapsulated, printed, integrated circuits mounted on a printed circuit board. Resistors, capacitors, and conductors are silk screened on a ceramic substrate, with semiconductors mounted before encapsulation.

Flip-Flop. A bistable multivibrator in which one transistor (or tube) conducts, while the other is cut off. A trigger signal reverses the situation. A following trigger signal restores the flip-flop to its original status. A flip-flop can be used as a frequency divider. If fed a 60 Hz signal, it will deliver a 30 Hz square wave output signal. Flip-flops are widely used in computers and electronic counters. (See Fig. 154.)

FM (Frequency Modulation). Invented by Edwin H. Armstrong; the frequency, instead of the amplitude, of a carrier signal is varied above and below the carrier's usual (unmodulated) frequency. The amplitude of the received signal, after demodulation, is proportional to the amount of frequency deviation (Fig. 210).

Frequency Changer. An electronic device or motor generator for changing frequency, such as from 60 Hz to 400 Hz.

185

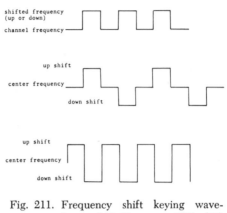

Fig. 210. Waveform of FM signal. Amplitude remains constant but cycles per second (hertz) varies with modulation.

shifted frequency
(up or down)

channel frequency

up shift

center frequency

down shift

up shift

center frequency

down shift

Fig. 211. Frequency shift keying waveforms. (A) Two-state FSK. (B) Three-state FSK. (C) Two-state FSK without neutral.

Frequency Deviation. In phase or frequency modulation, this term is used to indicate the peak difference between the instantaneous frequency of the modulated wave and the carrier frequency.

Frequency Multiplier. This is a circuit that is specifically designed to take a frequency and multiply it two or more times. (See Fig. 104.)

Frequency Response. This is a term usually associated with amplifiers. It refers to the frequency bandpass characteristics of the circuit. It can refer to an individual circuit or a complete system.

FSK (Frequency Shift Keying). A term used to define transmission of intelligence by shifting of the frequency of a carrier (AF or RF). In two-state FSK, the frequency is shifted in one direction only. In three-state FSK, the frequency is shifted above and below the center frequency (Fig. 211).

Full Duplex. A signal circuit in which both ends can transmit and receive simultaneously, as in telephony.

Gain. A general term used to indicate an increase in signal voltage, current, or power. Gain is usually expressed in decibels (db). (See Table 7.)

Table 7

DECIBELS VERSUS
POWER, VOLTAGE, AND CURRENT RATIOS

db	Current and Voltage Ratio		Power Ratio	
	Gain	Loss	Gain	Loss
0.1	1.012	0.9886	1.023	0.9772
0.2	1.023	.9772	1.047	.9550
0.3	1.035	.9661	1.072	.9333
0.4	1.047	.9550	1.097	.9120
0.5	1.059	.9441	1.122	.8913
0.6	1.072	.9333	1.148	.8710
0.7	1.084	.9226	1.175	.8511
0.8	1.097	.9120	1.202	.8318
0.9	1.109	.9016	1.230	.8128
1.0	1.122	.8913	1.259	.7943
1.1	1.135	.8811	1.288	.7763
1.2	1.148	.8710	1.318	.7586
1.3	1.162	.8610	1.349	.7413
1.4	1.175	.8511	1.380	.7244
1.5	1.189	.8414	1.413	.7080
1.6	1.202	.8318	1.445	.6918
1.7	1.216	.8222	1.479	.6761
1.8	1.230	.8128	1.514	.6607
1.9	1.245	.8035	1.549	.6457
2.0	1.259	.7943	1.585	.6310
2.1	1.274	.7852	1.622	.6166

Decibels Versus
Power, Voltage, and Current Ratios (Continued)

db	Current and Voltage Ratio		Power Ratio	
	Gain	Loss	Gain	Loss
2.2	1.288	.7763	1.660	.6026
2.3	1.303	.7674	1.698	.5888
2.4	1.318	.7586	1.738	.5754
2.5	1.334	.7499	1.778	.5623
2.6	1.349	.7413	1.820	.5495
2.7	1.365	.7328	1.862	.5370
2.8	1.380	.7244	1.905	.5248
2.9	1.396	.7161	1.950	.5129
3.0	1.413	.7080	1.995	.5012
3.1	1.429	.6998	2.042	.4898
3.2	1.445	.6918	2.089	.4786
3.3	1.462	.6839	2.138	.4677
3.4	1.479	.6761	2.188	.4571
3.5	1.496	.6683	2.239	.4467
3.6	1.514	.6607	2.291	.4365
3.7	1.531	.6531	2.344	.4266
3.8	1.549	.6457	2.399	.4169
3.9	1.567	.6383	2.455	.4074
4.0	1.585	.6310	2.512	.3981
4.1	1.603	.6237	2.570	.3891
4.2	1.622	.6166	2.630	.3802
4.3	1.641	.6095	2.692	.3715
4.4	1.660	.6026	2.754	.3631
4.5	1.679	.5957	2.818	.3548
4.6	1.698	.5888	2.884	.3467
4.7	1.718	.5821	2.951	.3389
4.8	1.738	.5754	3.020	.3311
4.9	1.758	.5689	3.090	.3236
5.0	1.778	.5623	3.162	.3162
5.1	1.799	.5559	3.236	.3090
5.2	1.820	.5495	3.311	.3020
5.3	1.841	.5433	3.388	.2951
5.4	1.862	.5370	3.467	.2884

Decibels Versus
Power, Voltage, and Current Ratios (Continued)

db	Current and Voltage Ratio		Power Ratio	
	Gain	Loss	Gain	Loss
5.5	1.884	.5309	3.548	.2818
5.6	1.905	.5248	3.631	.2754
5.7	1.928	.5188	3.715	.2692
5.8	1.950	.5129	3.802	.2630
5.9	1.973	.5070	3.891	.2570
6.0	1.995	.5012	3.981	.2512
6.1	2.018	.4958	4.074	.2455
6.2	2.042	.4898	4.169	.2399
6.3	2.065	.4842	4.266	.2344
6.4	2.089	.4786	4.365	.2291
6.5	2.114	.4732	4.467	.2239
6.6	2.138	.4677	4.571	.2188
6.7	2.163	.4624	4.677	.2138
6.8	2.188	.4571	4.786	.2089
6.9	2.213	.4519	4.898	.2042
7.0	2.239	.4467	5.012	.1995
7.1	2.265	.4416	5.129	.1950
7.2	2.291	.4365	5.248	.1906
7.3	2.317	.4315	5.370	.1862
7.4	2.344	.4266	5.495	.1820
7.5	2.371	.4217	5.623	.1778
7.6	2.399	.4169	5.754	.1738
7.7	2.427	.4121	5.888	.1698
7.8	2.455	.4074	6.026	.1660
7.9	2.483	.4027	6.166	.1622
8.0	2.512	.3981	6.310	.1585
8.1	2.541	.3936	6.457	.1549
8.2	2.570	.3891	6.607	.1514
8.3	2.600	.3846	6.761	.1479
8.4	2.630	.3802	6.918	.1445
8.5	2.661	.3758	7.079	.1413
8.6	2.692	.3715	7.244	.1380
8.7	2.723	.3673	7.413	.1349

Decibels Versus
Power, Voltage, and Current Ratios (Continued)

db	Current and Voltage Ratio		Power Ratio	
	Gain	Loss	Gain	Loss
8.8	2.754	.3631	7.586	.1318
8.9	2.786	.3589	7.762	.1288
9.0	2.818	.3548	7.943	.1259
9.1	2.851	.3508	8.128	.1230
9.2	2.884	.3467	8.318	.1202
9.3	2.917	.3428	8.511	.1175
9.4	2.951	.3389	8.710	.1148
9.5	2.985	.3350	8.913	.1122
9.6	3.020	.3311	9.120	.1097
9.7	3.055	.3273	9.333	.1072
9.8	3.090	.3236	9.550	.1047
9.9	3.126	.3199	9.772	.1023
10.0	3.162	.3162	10.000	.1000
10.1	3.199	.3126	10.23	.0977
10.2	3.236	.3090	10.47	.0955
10.3	3.273	.3055	10.72	.0933
10.4	3.311	.3020	10.97	.0912
10.5	3.350	.2985	11.22	.0891
10.6	3.388	.2951	11.48	.0871
10.7	3.428	.2917	11.75	.0851
10.8	3.467	.2884	12.02	.0832
10.9	3.508	.2851	12.30	.0813
11.0	3.548	.2818	12.59	.0794
11.1	3.589	.2786	12.88	.0776
11.2	3.631	.2754	13.18	.0759
11.3	3.673	.2723	13.49	.0741
11.4	3.715	.2692	13.81	.0724
11.5	3.758	.2661	14.13	.0708
11.6	3.802	.2630	14.45	.0692
11.7	3.846	.2600	14.79	.0676
11.8	3.891	.2570	15.14	.0660
11.9	3.936	.2541	15.49	.0646
12.0	3.981	.2512	15.85	.0631

Decibels Versus
Power, Voltage, and Current Ratios (Continued)

db	Current and Voltage Ratio		Power Ratio	
	Gain	Loss	Gain	Loss
12.1	4.027	.2483	16.22	.0617
12.2	4.074	.2455	16.60	.0603
12.3	4.121	.2427	16.98	.0589
12.4	4.169	.2399	17.38	.0575
12.5	4.217	.2371	17.78	.0562
12.6	4.266	.2344	18.20	.0550
12.7	4.315	.2317	18.62	.0537
12.8	4.365	.2291	19.05	.0525
12.9	4.416	.2265	19.50	.0513
13.0	4.467	.2239	19.95	.0501
13.1	4.519	.2213	20.42	.0490
13.2	4.571	.2188	20.89	.0479
13.3	4.624	.2163	21.38	.0468
13.4	4.677	.2138	21.88	.0457
13.5	4.732	.2113	22.39	.0447
13.6	4.786	.2089	22.91	.0437
13.7	4.842	.2065	23.44	.0427
13.8	4.898	.2042	23.99	.0417
13.9	4.955	.2018	24.55	.0407
14.0	5.012	.1995	25.12	.0398
14.1	5.070	.1972	25.70	.0389
14.2	5.129	.1950	26.30	.0380
14.3	5.188	.1928	26.92	.0372
14.4	5.248	.1906	27.54	.0363
14.5	5.309	.1884	28.18	.0355
14.6	5.370	.1862	28.84	.0347
14.7	5.433	.1841	29.51	.0339
14.8	5.495	.1820	30.20	.0331
14.9	5.559	.1799	30.90	.0324
15.0	5.623	.1778	31.62	.0316
15.1	5.689	.1758	32.36	.0309
15.2	5.754	.1738	33.11	.0302
15.3	5.821	.1718	33.88	.0295

Decibels Versus
Power, Voltage, and Current Ratios (Continued)

db	Current and Voltage Ratio		Power Ratio	
	Gain	Loss	Gain	Loss
15.4	5.888	.1698	34.67	.0288
15.5	5.957	.1679	35.48	.0282
15.6	6.026	.1660	36.31	.0275
15.7	6.096	.1641	37.15	.0269
15.8	6.166	.1622	38.02	.0263
15.9	6.237	.1603	38.91	.0257
16.0	6.310	.1585	39.81	.0251
16.1	6.383	.1566	40.74	.0245
16.2	6.457	.1549	41.69	.0239
16.3	6.531	.1531	42.66	.0234
16.4	6.607	.1514	43.65	.0229
16.5	6.683	.1496	44.67	.0224
16.6	6.761	.1479	45.71	.0219
16.7	6.839	.1462	46.77	.0214
16.8	6.918	.1445	47.86	.0209
16.9	6.998	.1429	48.98	.0204
17.0	7.079	.1413	50.12	.0200
17.1	7.161	.1396	51.29	.0195
17.2	7.244	.1380	52.43	.0191
17.3	7.328	.1365	53.70	.0186
17.4	7.413	.1349	54.96	.0182
17.5	7.499	.1334	56.23	.0178
17.6	7.586	.1318	57.54	.0174
17.7	7.674	.1303	58.88	.0170
17.8	7.762	.1288	60.26	.0166
17.9	7.852	.1273	61.66	.0162
18.0	7.943	.1259	63.10	.0158
18.1	8.035	.1245	64.57	.0155
18.2	8.128	.1230	66.07	.0151
18.3	8.222	.1216	67.61	.0148
18.4	8.318	.1202	69.18	.0145
18.5	8.414	.1189	70.80	.0141
18.6	8.511	.1175	72.44	.0138

Decibels Versus
Power, Voltage, and Current Ratios (Continued)

db	Current and Voltage Ratio		Power Ratio	
	Gain	Loss	Gain	Loss
18.7	8.610	.1161	74.13	.0135
18.8	8.710	.1148	75.86	.0132
18.9	8.811	.1135	77.63	.0129
19.0	8.913	.1122	79.43	.0126
19.1	9.016	.1109	81.28	.0123
19.2	9.120	.1097	83.18	.0120
19.3	9.226	.1083	85.11	.0117
19.4	9.333	.1072	87.10	.0115
19.5	9.441	.1059	89.13	.0112
19.6	9.550	.1047	91.20	.0110
19.7	9.661	.1035	93.33	.0107
19.8	9.772	.1023	95.50	.0105
19.9	9.886	.1012	97.72	.0102
20.0	10.00	.1000	100.0	.0100
30.0	31.62	.0316	1,000.0	.0010
40.0	100.0	.0100	10^4	10^{-4}
50.0	316.2	.0032	10^5	10^{-5}
60.0	1,000.0	.0010	10^6	10^{-6}
70.0	3,162.0	.0003	10^7	10^{-7}
80.0	10,000.0	.0001	10^8	10^{-8}
90.0	31,620.0	.00003	10^9	10^{-9}
100.0	100,000.0	.00001	10^{10}	10^{-10}

Gain Control. A device used to vary the gain of a circuit. It is usually a variable resistor, often called a potentiometer.

Gauss. The unit of magnetic induction (flux density).

Generator. AF and RF (Audio Frequencies and Radio Frequencies). A test instrument used in the testing and alignment of various electronic units. Some signal generators combine the AF and RF features in one instrument. RF and AF signals may be utilized separately or with the AF modulating the RF signal. (See Figs. 169, 170, and 171.)

Generator, Sweep. A test instrument which is an RF generator capable of generating an RF signal the frequency of which is swept over a band of frequencies. When it is used in conjunction with an oscilloscope, a usual display of the bandpass characteristics of a circuit under test can be observed (Fig. 212).

Getter. A metal within a vacuum tube; its function is to absorb residued gas and any gas that might be liberated by heating of tube elements. (See Fig. 96.)

Gigacycle. This term is obsolete, refers to Gigahertz.

Gigahertz. A term used to indicate billions of cycles per second.

Handset. A single-piece device containing a telephone transmitter at one end and a telephone receiver at the other. Most telephones employ a handset. For use in two-way radio systems, the handset also contains a press-to-talk switch. When the switch is pressed, the radio transmitter is turned on; when it is released, the radio transmitter is turned off and the radio receiver is activated (Fig. 213).

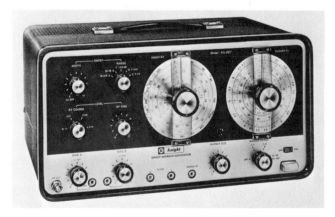

Fig. 212. Sweep generator.

Fig. 213. Handset (Courtesy
of Shure Bros.).

Fig. 214. Headset (Courtesy of Su-
perex).

Harmonic. A multiple of a frequency. An oscillator operating at 1000 KHz, for example, might also produce signals at 2000 KHz (second harmonic), 3000KHz (third harmonic), and other multiples of 1000 KHz.

Headset. A transducer for private listening employing one or two earphones (one for each ear) and a headband for hands-free use (Fig. 214).

Heat Sink. A device on which a transistor is mounted in order to dissipate rapidly any heat that a transistor develops. It is usually made of aluminum and has heat radiating fins (Fig. 215).

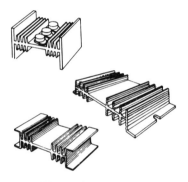

Fig. 215. Heat sinks.

Henry. The unit of self or mutual inductance (L).

Heptode. An electron tube having seven electrodes.

HF (High Frequency). This term is used to identify the portion of the radio spectrum between 3000 KHz and 30 MHz.

High Fidelity. An abused term applied to sound systems and radios to denote that sound is faithfully reproduced.

Hollogram. A photographic recorder that re-creates three dimensional images. It is used to store and retrieve information for switching, data transmission, and other communication applications.

IF. An abbreviation for intermediate frequency.

Image Orthicon. A television camera picture tube used primarily in broadcast applications to televise. The electron image is scanned by a low velocity beam from the back of a mosaic called the target.

Impedance. To an AC signal, impedance is much like what resistance is to a DC signal. The resistance of a coil or transformer winding may be very low, but its impedance very high. Impedance is a function of inductive and capacitive reactance, and it is affected by resistance.

Impedance Matching. Maximum power is transferred when the source and load impedances are equal. When they are not equal, impedance matching transformers may be used. For example, a 600-ohm source may be matched to a 50-ohm load by employing a transformer with a 12:1 impedance ratio.

Inductance. Usually a coil of wire wound on a form or iron core. The unit of inductance is the henry (L). The greater the number of turns, the greater the inductance. Changing the core material or its orientation will also change inductance.

Inductance, Variable. A coil the inductance of which can be changed. One method is to vary the spacing between turns; the other is to employ a powdered iron core, which is moved through the center of the coil. Both methods cause a change in inductance. (See Fig. 37.)

Inductor. A coil of any type possessing inductance. It may be wound on an insulated form (air core) or on an iron core; or it may be wound on a form within which is an adjustable ferrite (powdered iron) core.

Inductor, Air Core. A coil without a core. It is used primarily in RF circuits for frequency determination, or a load. (See Fig. 36.)

Inductor, Ferrite Core. A coil with a ferrite core. Coils of this type are widely used in RF and video circuits because of their high "Q" and because inductance can be changed by adjustment of the ferrite core. (See Fig. 37.)

Inductor, Iron Core. Usually an inductance with a laminated or powdered iron core. The iron core has the effect of increasing the inductance.

Integrated Circuit. This device consists of various transistors, resistors, capacitors, etc., that have been made up to

197

Fig. 216. Integrated circuit module (Courtesy of Amperex Corp.).

Fig. 217. Master intercom unit (Courtesy of Dictograph).

form a chip. Several chips can be combined in one unit to make up one I.C. (Fig. 216).

Intercom, Wired. An intercommunications system using wires as the transmission medium. A system may consist of one master unit (Fig. 217) and one slave unit, one master and several selectable slave units, all master units, or a combination of master and slave units. (See Fig. 149.)

Intercom, Wireless. An intercommunications system using the power lines as the transmission medium. Each station employs a low power radio transceiver. (See Fig. 150.)

Inverse Feedback. A term used to describe an out-of-phase voltage feeding back into a circuit to improve the frequency characteristics of that circuit. At the same time, the gain is reduced (Fig. 218).

Inverter. A device for converting DC to AC, or DC to DC at another voltage.

Kilocycle. This term is no longer used. (See Kilohertz.)

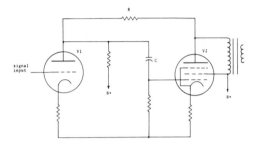

Fig. 218. Example of inverse feedback. A part of the signal at the plate of V2 is fed through R to the plate of V1 (and through C to the grid of V2) 180° out of phase. This reduces the gain of V2, but also reduces distortion.

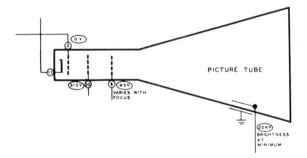

Fig. 219. Television picture tube (Courtesy of Heath Co.).

199

Kilohertz. This term is used to indicate a frequency of 1000 hertz: 10 kilohertz (KHz) is equal to 10,000 hertz.

Kinescope. The picture tube in a television receiver (Fig. 219).

Kludge. A humorous term used to refer to a "black box" or computer.

LF (Low Frequency). This is the band of frequencies in the radio spectrum which lies between 30 KHz and 300 KHz.

Limiter, Amplitude. An electronic device that limits the amplitude of a signal. It is usually designed to have no effect when the signal is weak, but to limit the amplitude of the signal if it tends to rise above a predetermined level. (See Fig. 113.)

Line Filter. A filter installed between an electronic device and the power source. It is designed to reduce or eliminate signals or interference that might come into the equipment through the power line. (See Fig. 56.)

Line, Unbalanced. An unbalanced line usually refers to a transmission or signal-carrying line in which one of the two wires is at ground potential. A coaxial cable (Fig. 158) is an unbalanced line the shield of which is one of the conductors (ground) (Fig. 220).

Log. A record of everything pertinent to the operation of a computer. Any runs, work done, changes made, everything— must be written in the log.

Loudspeaker. A device used to convert electric current variations into audible sound. The most commonly used type is the PM (permanent magnet) loudspeaker. The audio signal passes through the voice coil and produces a varying magnetic field that interacts with the permanent magnet field; this action causes the voice coil to move in and out and the cone to vibrate and produce sound waves (Fig. 221).

Low Pass Filter. A wave filter which passes all signals below its cut-off frequency, and attenuates all signals at higher frequencies (Fig. 222).

Magnetic Disc. A flat circular plate with a magnetic surface on which data can be stored by alteration of the magnetic

200

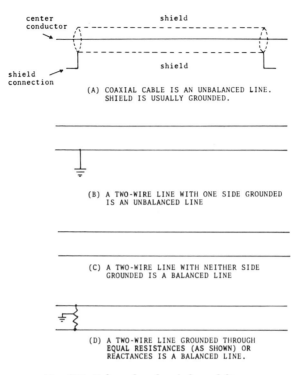

center
conductor
shield

shield
connection

shield

shield

(A) COAXIAL CABLE IS AN UNBALANCED LINE.
    SHIELD IS USUALLY GROUNDED.

(B) A TWO-WIRE LINE WITH ONE SIDE GROUNDED
    IS AN UNBALANCED LINE

(C) A TWO-WIRE LINE WITH NEITHER SIDE
    GROUNDED IS A BALANCED LINE

(D) A TWO-WIRE LINE GROUNDED THROUGH
    EQUAL RESISTANCES (AS SHOWN) OR
    REACTANCES IS A BALANCED LINE.

Fig. 220. Balanced and unbalanced lines.

field on various portions of the disc. Usually, the disc rotates
at high speed with data applied or removed by magnetic
heads in much the same manner as when magnetic tape is
used.

Master Data. A set of data which is rarely changed and
provides basic data for processing information.

Megacycle. This term is no longer used. (See Megahertz.)

Megahertz. This term is used to indicate a frequency of
1,000,000 hertz (cycles per second).

Memory Core. A storage device composed of ferromagnetic
cores, or an apertured ferrite plate, through which select lines
and sense windings are threaded.

201

Fig. 221. Loudspeaker.

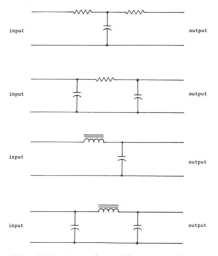

Fig. 222. Examples of low pass filters.

Microfarad. A unit of capacitance. One microfarad is equal to one millionth of a farad.

Microhenry. A unit of inductance. One microhenry is equal to one millionth of a henry.

Fig. 223. Hand-held microphone (Courtesy of
Electro-Voice, Inc.).

Microphone. A device that converts mechanical changes
into electrical changes (Fig. 223). Varying air movement on
its diaphragm causes a varying electrical voltage to be developed at its output terminals. Hence, a microphone is a
sound-powered generator. A carbon microphone, on the other
hand, changes its resistance and does not generate a voltage.

Microwave. An electromagnetic radio wave operating in the
microwave region of the spectrum (above 890 MHz).

Millihenry. A unit of inductance. One millihenry is equal to
one thousandth of a henry.

Mixer. A circuit that has two different signals going in and
a third coming out (Fig. 224).

Mobile Radio. Radio communications between mobile radio
stations as well as with radio stations at fixed locations (base
stations). Generally applicable to land communications. (See
Fig. 145.)

Mobile Unit. A mobile two-way radiotelephone consisting
of a transmitter and a receiver. The term "mobile" means that

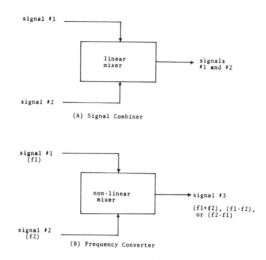

(A) Signal Combiner

(B) Frequency Converter

Fig. 224. Signal mixers.

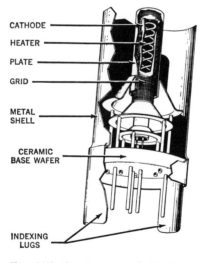

Fig. 225. Construction of Nuvistor-type triode tube (Courtesy of Radio Corporation of America).

it can be operated in transit, installed in a vehicle of any type or carried by a person. (See Fig. 195.)

Modulator. A device that varies the amplitude, frequency, or phase of a carrier signal for the purpose of transmitting intelligence.

Monochrome. A word used in television to describe a black and white picture.

MTBF. Abbreviation for "mean time before failure," a term used for establishing reliability parameters.

Multivibrator. A relaxation oscillator used to generate non-sinusoidal electrical waves. It employs two tubes or transistors connected so that the output of each is coupled to the input of the other in order to maintain oscillation. Some types oscillate only when triggered. (See Fig. 154.)

Mutual Conductance. A term used in reference to vacuum tubes to indicate the effect on plate current due to grid voltage changes.

NIH Factor. A term used by engineers meaning the "not invented here factor." Its implication is that the engineers involved are reluctant to use known techniques and prefer to circumvent them by improvising.

Nuvistor. A type of vacuum tube, not much larger than a transistor, which is particularly efficient at high frequencies (Fig. 225).

Ohmmeter. A test instrument used to measure the value of an unknown resistance by measuring current flow with a milliammeter or microammeter calibrated in ohms and megohms.

"OR" Circuit. A circuit used in computers. It usually consists of a circuit in which two inputs control one output. Either input can be used to control the output. Figure 226 illustrates the principle of an "OR" circuit.

Oscillator. An electronic generator of AF or RF signals.

Oscillator, AF (Oscillator, Audio Frequency). An electronic generator of audio frequency signals. (See Fig. 169.)

Oscillator, Colpitts. An electronic AF or RF generator employing a single untapped coil shunted by two capacitors in

205

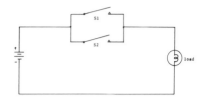

Fig. 226. Principle of OR circuit.
Voltage will be applied
to the load if either S1
OR S2 is closed.

series which function as a voltage divider and determine the amount of feedback, as well as the frequency of oscillation. (See Fig. 93.)

Oscillator, Crystal-Controlled. An RF oscillator using a piezoelectric crystal to sustain oscillation and maintain constant frequency. (See Fig. 198.)

Oscillator, Hartley. An electronic AF or RF generator employing a single tapped coil shunted by a capacitor. The value of total inductance and capacitance determines the oscillating frequency. The position of the tap determines the amount of feedback. (See Fig. 94.)

Oscillator, L-C (Oscillator, Inductance-Capacitance). An oscillator in which the L (inductance) and C (capacitance) determine the frequency of operation. Oscillation occurs at the frequency at which the L and C reactances are equal. (See Figs. 93 and 94.)

Oscillator, RF (Oscillator, Radio Frequency). An electronic generator of RF energy.

Oscilloscope. An electronic measuring instrument employing a cathode ray tube. It can be used to observe waveforms and to measure voltage, current, power, phase, and frequency. It is actually a voltmeter that indicates voltage with respect to time. (See Fig. 167.)

Parasitics. Undesirable oscillations that cause improper operation. They can be the result of poor bypassing, poor coupling between circuits, improper neutralization, and so on.

PA System (Public Address System). A sound reinforce-

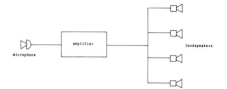

Fig. 227. Basic public address system.

ment or distribution system employing one or more microphones, an AF amplifier, and one or more loudspeakers (Fig. 227).

Pentagrid Converter. A seven-electrode vacuum tube with five grids, most commonly used as a frequency converter. The first grid, nearest the cathode, is used as the grid of an oscillator circuit, and the second grid as the plate. Grid 1 modulates the cathode-to-plate electron stream at the oscillation frequency rate. The input signal is fed to grid 3, which modulates the electron stream at its oscillation frequency. Grid 4 is the screen grid, which provides isolation from the plate, and grid 5 is the suppressor grid, which retards secondary emission from the plate to the screen. Plate current is modulated at two different frequencies, the sum or difference beat of which can be selected with the use of a resonant circuit as the plate load, tuned to the desired beat frequency. (See Fig. 106.)

Pentode. A vacuum tube having five elements. (See Figs. 96 and 97.)

Phone Patch. A device for linking a radio station to a telephone circuit. It enables a person at a distant telephone to talk over the radio transmitter and listen to the output of the radio receiver (Fig. 228).

Phono Plug. A two-circuit plug generally used with single-conductor shielded cable, with the inside conductor connected to the pin of the plug and the shield to its shell. Originally designed for connecting a phonograph pickup to an amplifier, phono plugs are now in wide use for other applications (Fig. 229).

207

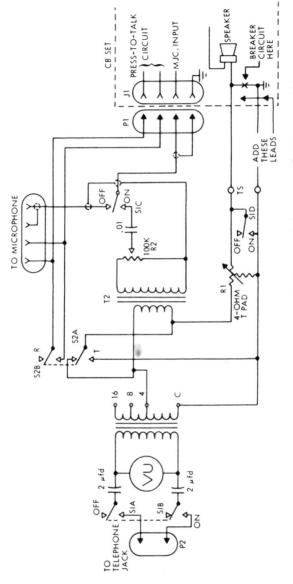

Fig. 228. Schematic diagram of a typical phone patch (Courtesy of *CB* magazine).

Fig. 229. Phono plug.

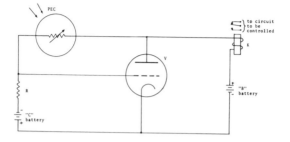

Fig. 230. Photoelectric cell control circuit. When no
light impinges on the PE cell, its resistance
is extremely high. The tube is biased to
cutoff by the "C" battery through R. When
light impinges on the PE cell, its resistance
lowers and positive voltage from the plate
of V offsets the negative bias. The tube
conducts and relay K is energized.

Fig. 231. Phonograph cartridge at end of tone arm (left).
(Courtesy of Shure Bros.).

Photoelectric Cell. An electron tube that utilizes a light-
sensitive cathode. The output depends on the photoelectric
emission from the irradiated area of the photo cathode, and
varies with the intensity of the light impinging on the cathode
(Fig. 230).

Pickup. Common term for phonograph transducer, interchangeable with the term "phonograph cartridge." It has a
stylus (or needle) that rides in the phonograph record groove

and drives a magnetic, ceramic, or crystal voltage generator (Fig. 231).

Picofarad. A unit of capacitance. One picofarad is equal to a millionth of a millionth of a farad. Formerly it was called the micro-microfarad.

Pi-Network. A low pass filter that can be resonated at a specific frequency and whose input and output impedances may differ. It usually consists of an inductance in series with the signal path and a capacitor at each end, with the other terminals of the capacitors grounded. Input and output impedances and resonant frequency can be adjusted with the capacitor or by variation of the value of inductance, or by adjustment of all three elements (Fig. 232).

Potentiometer. A variable resistance generally used as a voltage divider. It functions as a gain control by permitting adjustment of the signal level. It is also used to adjust operating voltages (Fig. 233).

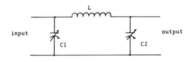

Fig. 232. Single section Pi network. Although not shown as such, L may also be variable.

Fig. 233. Potentiometer (Courtesy of Memcor, Inc.).

Fig. 234. Printed circuit module.

Power. A term to express the rate of doing work in a certain period of time. The symbol is W (watts) or P (power).

Power Transmogrifier. A device for changing the character of power (see Converter and Inverter).

Printed Circuit. A phenolic board on which electrical conductors are applied photographically, eliminating the need for wires (Fig. 234).

Program. In computer work, a plan for the automatic solutions of problems. A complete program includes plans for transcription of data, coding information for the computer, and plans for utilization of the result.

PRT (Program Reference Table). The PRT (in computer work) contains the locations reserved for program variables, data descriptions that give information about data arrays, and other information.

Pulse Repetition Rate. The number of pulses transmitted each second is called the pulse repetition rate.

Q. This is called the figure of merit of an energy-storing system. It is usually associated with a coil or capacitor.

Fig. 235. Radar for weather observation (Courtesy of Kaar
Electronics Corp.).

Radar. "Radio detection and ranging." Radar is used by
industry for weather observation and on boats for navigation.
A radar transmits a short burst of RF energy which is reflected
back to the radar when it strikes a solid object or moisture
particles. The radar measures the time required for the pulse
to travel to its target and return, and indicates the distance to
the target on the screen of a cathode ray tube (Fig. 235).

Radiator. The part of an antenna that radiates the signal
(Fig. 236).

Rectifier. A device that rectifies (permits current to flow
through it in one direction only). It can be used in power
supplies to convert AC to DC. An AM demodulator is also a
rectifier.

Rectifier, Bridge. A full-wave rectifying circuit with four
rectifiers connected in a bridge circuit. (See Fig. 64.)

Rectifier, Controlled. A triode or pentode tube, or a transistor, can be used as a controlled rectifier by application of

212

a control signal to the grid (tube) or base (transistor). However, an SCR (silicon-controlled rectifier) is designed specifically for this purpose. It consists of a silicon rectifier with three elements—anode, cathode, and gate. It will not conduct until a trigger voltage is applied to the gate. The average current flow through the SCR (or average voltage across the load) can be controlled by adjustment of the time that a trigger voltage is present during each cycle. (See Figs. 134, 135, and 138.)

Fig. 236. Radiator of antenna (Courtesy of Mark Products).

Rectifier, Copper Oxide. A rectifier utilizing a barrier layer developed between copper and cuprous oxide. This type of rectifier has long life, but low efficiency.

Rectifier, Electrolytic. This rectifier converts AC to DC by utilizing an electrolyte. It consists of two electrodes and an electrolyte that produces a polarizing film on one of the electrodes, thus permitting current to flow readily through it in one direction only.

Rectifier, Full-Wave. This is a rectifier system developed to rectify both halves of the AC wave. Because of this feature, the hum content is reduced and it is much easier to filter. A 60 Hz AC wave is converted to a 120 Hz pulsating DC. (See Figs. 64 and 65.)

Rectifier, Germanium. A semiconductor diode employing germanium.

Rectifier, Half-Wave. A rectifier which conducts during each half-cycle only. When it is used to rectify 60 Hz AC, for example, the output will consist of 60 rounded pulses per second separated by periods of no output between them. When its output is bridged by a capacitor, DC voltage will be available continuously, since the capacitor charges during the half-cycles that the rectifier conducts. (See Fig. 62.)

Rectifier, Selenium. A rectifier utilizing a barrier layer formed between specially treated crystallized selenium and an alloy of cadmium. The selenium is placed on a sheet of steel or aluminum to promote heat transfer (Fig. 237).

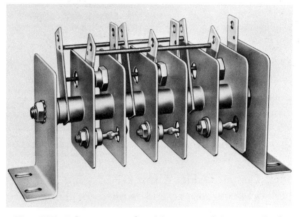

Fig. 237. Selenium rectifier (Courtesy of Syntron Co.).

Rectifier, Silicon. A diode employing silicon as the semiconductor material. Considered highly reliable and remarkably efficient. (See Fig. 61.)

Rectifier, Thermionic. A vacuum tube used as a rectifier (usually two-element).

214

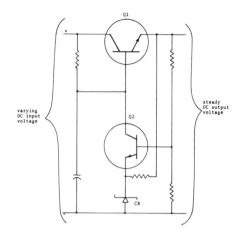

Fig. 238. Typical series voltage regulator. The conductivity of transistor Q1 is changed as output voltage tends to vary, as sensed by Q2. Zener diode CR serves as a voltage reference.

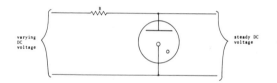

Fig. 239. Shunt voltage regulator employing VR tube.

Register. In computer work, a device that is used for the storage of one or more computer bits/words.

Regulator, Series. An electronic device connected in series between the power source and the load. This regulator acts as a variable resistor; its value changes as the load current or input voltage changes, thus maintaining constant output voltage (Fig. 238).

Regulator Tube. This term refers to a tube that utilizes a gas inside it and depends on the discharge through it to maintain a constant voltage across it. This tube is connected across a DC source in series with a resistor. It has the ability to maintain the voltage constant across its terminals for a rather wide variation of input voltage (Fig. 239).

Relay. An electromagnetic switching device. Electrical contacts are arranged so that they will make contact when the coil is de-energized. When the coil is de-energized, the contacts will break. Many variations of make and break contacts can be provided. (See Fig. 34.)

Resonance, Parallel. When a capacitor and an inductor are connected in parallel, the circuit will be resonant at the frequency at which the inductive and capacitive reactances are equal. At this frequency only, the impedance of the circuit is extremely high. (See Fig. 48.)

RETMA (Radio Electronics Television Manufacturers Association) Color Code. A color code evolved for the identification of transformers, resistors, and condensers. Different colors are assigned to indicate voltage rating, capacity, resistance, etc. Now called EIA (Electronic Industries Association) color code.

RF. An abbreviation for radio frequency.

Screen Room. A test room completely enclosed by a screen mesh. Its purpose is to prevent extraneous electrical signals and noise from entering the test area and affecting the results of tests.

Secode Selector. An electromechanical decoder which responds to pulses from a telephone dial. Code pins can be installed to set the decoder to respond to any one of more than 300,000 combinations. (See Fig. 202.)

Sine Wave. A wave form that is the sine of a linear function of time, or space, or both. (See Fig. 75[A].)

Skin Effect. A term used to describe radio frequencies when they travel through a conductor. They tend to travel along the outside circumference of the conductor, and thus the term "skin effect."

"S" Meter. A meter used in communications receivers to indicate relative signal strength. It is usually wired to give

Fig. 240. "S" meter.

a reading proportionate to the level of the input signal. The meter is calibrated in "S" units from 0 to 9, and in db units in powers of 10 above S9 (Fig. 240).

TDM. Abbreviation for time division multiplex. (See Fig. 160.)

Thermistor. A resistor that has a high negative coefficient of resistance. As the temperature increases, the resistance decreases. A thermistor is often used when it is necessary to maintain a steady voltage in circuits in which heat is generated nearby (Fig. 241).

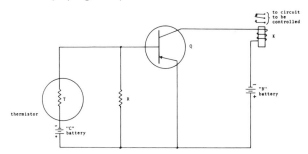

Fig. 241. Simple thermistor circuit. Ordinarily, transistor Q does not conduct since its forward bias is too low because the resistance of the thermistor is too high. When the temperature of the thermistor rises, its resistance lowers, raising the forward bias on Q. Collector current rises and relay K is energized.

Thyratron. A gas-filled triode or tetrode tube used for control purposes. (See Figs. 132 and 137.)

Thyristor. A semiconductor device that operates on the P-N-P-N regenerative principle. There are many types and variations in use, but generally they are used as a controlling device in an electronic circuit. Ideal applications include use for triggering, use in timing circuits, and use for logic functions.

Tone Channel. A one-way tone signaling circuit consisting of a tone transmitter and a tone receiver. Intelligence is transmitted by keying of the tone on and off or by shifting of its frequency. (See FSK.) (See Fig. 161.)

Transducer. A device which converts physical changes into an electrical signal (such as a microphone), or one which converts an electrical signal into physical changes (such as a loudspeaker).

Transformer, Filament. This is a device that is used to supply low voltage to the filaments of tubes. It consists of a core of laminated iron around which is wound the primary that is fed by the AC power line. The secondary voltage is fed to the filaments. (See Fig. 73.)

Tube Tester. A test instrument used to test vacuum tubes. It applies appropriate voltages to the filament and other elements and then evaluates the quality of the tube on a meter. This is done by measuring the transconductance (Gm) or cathode emission of the tube. (See Fig. 172.)

Tweeter. A loudspeaker specially designed to reproduce only the high audio frequencies. It is used in conjunction with a woofer and a crossover network. The crossover network permits only the high frequency signal to get into the tweeter and the low frequency signals into the woofer.

Twintron. An electromechanical resonator which can be used as the frequency determining element in an oscillator, or as a bandpass or band-rejection filter. (See Fig. 156.)

UHF. An abbreviation for the term ultra high frequency. The UHF spectrum lies between the frequencies of 300 MHz and 3 GHz.

218

Fig. 242. Variable frequency oscillator.

Ultrasonic. The frequency range above audibility, extending
into the low RF range.

VFO. An abbreviation for variable frequency oscillator
(Fig. 242).

Video Signal. A television signal. The term is also used in
reference to frequencies above audibility. Figure 243 is a
schematic diagram of a video amplifier.

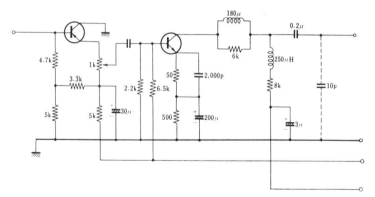

Fig. 243. Video amplifier circuit coil in collector circuit of second transistor improves high frequency response (Courtesy of Hitachi,
Ltd.).

Vidicon. A television camera picture tube used mostly in CCTV systems. It is much less costly than the image orthicon tube used in television broadcast cameras and quite adequate for most industrial applications. (See Fig. 147.)

VOM (**Volt-Ohm-Milliammeter**). A test meter used to test electrical circuits. It is designed to measure AC volts, DC volts, DC milliamperes and ohms. (See Fig. 164.)

VTVM (**Vacuum Tube Voltmeter**). A test meter designed for the testing and checking of electronic circuits. It is designed so that, when it is used to test circuits, it will not load the circuit down. Its input resistance for DC is usually in megohms, for AC, about 200,000 to 500,000 ohms. (See Fig. 165.)

VU (**Volume Units**). This is a unit of measurement associated with audio work. A VU meter has a reference 0 near the upper end of the scale. This is a loosely used term to indicate either the intensity of sound or the magnitude of an electrical wave.

Wireless. Obsolete term for "radio," still used by the British.

Woofer. A loudspeaker designed specifically to reproduce only low audio frequencies. It is used in conjunction with a tweeter and a crossover network. This network allows the high frequencies to pass through to the tweeter, the low frequencies to the woofer.

• ABOUT THE AUTHOR

Leo G. Sands is the author of more than 30 books on telecommunications and electronics, more than 800 magazine articles, and numerous home-study course texts. Among other Chilton books, he has written or co-authored are *Guide to Mobile Radio, VHF-FM Marine Radio*, and *Portable FM Radiotelephones*. He is the editor of *CB Magazine* and the *Proceedings of the Radio Club of America*, and is a Senior Member of the Institute of Electrical and Electronics Engineers, and a Fellow of the Radio Club of America.

Mr. Sands became a licensed amateur radio operator (W7PH) in 1926 and a licensed commercial radiotelephone operator in 1944. After completing the Smith-Hughes electrical trade course in high school, he studied electrical engineering at the University of California and has lectured at the University of Washington, Georgia Tech, and the Maryland Academy of Sciences.

In 1946 he pioneered in the application of VHF-FM railroad and marine radio, designing systems for numerous railroads and tugboat operators.

Mr. Sands has been employed as an executive by RCA, Bendix, and Philco; since 1954, he has served as a consultant to the electronics industry. He is now president of Leo G. Sands Associates, Inc., headquartered in New York City. His firm is engaged in the electronic systems engineering field, market research, and in conducting training programs in electronics for electricians.